Raising Pigs

The Ultimate Guide to Pig Raising on Your Homestead

Contents

Introduction

Raising pigs is a profitable venture made easy with this guide in hand. Each chapter provides detailed information to help both beginners and experienced pig farmers in their journey raising pigs. By simply following the recommendations in this book, it is possible to enjoy life while raising pigs, unburdened by the challenges that most pig keeper's face.

Some books on the market claim to have in-depth knowledge to pig keeping. This book is up to date, featuring all the modern practices associated with modern-day farming. This book has been written in easy to understand language for both beginners and experienced pig farmers.

Raising pigs requires a hands-on approach. For this reason, this book contains hands-on methods and instructions using accessible and relatable language. Additionally, the book meets the needs of various pig farmers from across the globe. Whether you are in the United States or South Africa, this book's practical actions are beneficial to all pig keepers, regardless of the size of your pig operation or location.

Chapter 1: Why Raise Pigs: Meat, Compost, or Pets

Despite their reputation, pigs are not "filthy" or "dirty" animals. In fact, they are clean animals that roll in the mud as a cooling mechanism in a hot environment. Pigs that live in cold climates need not roll in the mud, and as a result, stay "clean." Pigs are great domestic animals that can be kept as a source of food or as pets. The following are facts that will help you to understand pigs better.

Facts About Pigs and Their Purpose

History

Pigs, also known as hogs or swine, are domesticated animals whose meat is popularly consumed worldwide. Historians started documenting the breeding of these animals in Europe, Asia, and the northern parts of Africa about 9,000 years ago. Since then, many farmers raised pigs, and by the late 20th century, pigs were a household name, owing to the then improved breeding and feeding techniques.

There are many species of pigs, including the wild boar, which is an uncastrated male domestic pig. The term boar is generally used when referring to a wild pig. A pig can weigh from 300 lbs. (136 kg) to 1000 lbs. (454 kg). On average, a swine can grow up to 2.5 feet (70 cm) long.

Today, there are over two billion domestic pigs worldwide. These animals are distributed across different parts of the world. They can survive in different habitats, and scientists have attributed this incredible resilience to their high intelligence levels. But pigs are comfortable in colder environments and hot climates.

Environment

Contrary to popular belief, pigs are relatively clean animals. Rolling in the mud helps them regulate their body temperature because they cannot sweat biologically like humans or other animals. And it allows them to create an unfavorable environment for parasites. These fascinating creatures keep their waste secretions far from where they live or eat.

Intelligence

Pigs are intelligent animals. People that work with pigs know that they are very smart animals. For instance, did you know that pigs can remember objects, places, and other items to help them navigate their environment? They have excellent memories and can recall information for years. And they can also perceive time! Pigs are curious and like to forage while exploring the ground.

Social Capabilities

Although it doesn't always seem like the first choice, many people keep pigs as pets. Being quite playful, along with their social attributes, pigs have been described by many people as great pets due to the variety of characteristics these animals display.

They prefer to travel in close groups known as sounders, made up of females and their young offspring. These groups help them keep warm during the cold seasons. Pigs must be kept in their social circles since isolation causes stress and discomfort, but when they are pregnant or sick, isolation is the go-to strategy.

Communication and Defense

Pigs communicate using grunts and squeaks. A pig's grunt depends on the animal's "personality" and exposure to danger. Grunts and long squeals are a pig's way of alerting others about imminent threats. In such a case, a pig's primary defense mechanism will be to flee, and you'll be surprised to discover that pigs are well-known sprinters. They can run as fast as ten miles per hour (17 km/h), and wild pigs can run at speeds of up to 30 miles per hour (50 km/h). This short outburst of pace is not sustainable as they tire out quickly. If running is not an option, pigs can use their tusks as weapons if they feel threatened. Some have sizable tusks that are razor sharp and can inflict significant damage. Show caution when handling sows with piglets, but pigs are generally not aggressive animals.

Reproduction

A pig takes about four months to reproduce. This is by far a desirable feature in livestock, especially compared to a cow which gestates for approximately nine months. Additionally, a swine can have a litter of about six to twelve piglets compared to a cow, which gives birth to one or two calves at most at a time. Unlike any other livestock animals, a piglet can double in size a week after its birth. You'll find that newborn piglets quickly learn to respond to their mother's voice, and usually the mother uses grunts to communicate with her offspring while nursing them. This is why in the past, farmers would prefer to raise pigs more than any other animal as they can produce a lot of meat at a much faster rate.

Vision and Hearing

Last, pigs do not have good vision. They can distinguish between colors, but their range of vision is limited. To make up for it, they have a great sense of smell and hearing. You will quickly notice that pigs are not comfortable around loud sounds. Prolonged exposure to such noises startle pigs and can cause them a lot of stress, so consider maintaining a quiet approach. Don't enter piggeries slamming doors or making loud noises. As pets, they enjoy listening to soft music and getting occasional massages.

Reasons for Keeping Pigs

Meat

Raising hogs for commercial meat is one of the most profitable farm ventures, regardless of the farm's size. Globally, keeping pigs for commercial purposes is quite a lucrative business. For instance, China has the largest number of pigs of any country, with over 310 million, followed by Europe, the USA, and Brazil.

Advantages of Keeping Pigs for Commercial Meat

Pig products such as pork and bacon are always in demand. There is a growing demand for both from traditional farm-kept pigs. Approximately 35% of all meat consumed by humans is pork. And what's even better is this percentage is growing at a steady rate every year. There could not be a better era to raise pigs for meat as the global production output has fallen by approximately 7% because of the crisis in 2020, and an additional 2% decrease in the worldwide production of pork courtesy of the African swine flu, which plagued the Asian market. This has seen farmers expand their herds to cope with the increasing demand for pork.

Keeping hogs for meat is relatively straightforward and basic. Most farmers already have a rough idea of the kind of meat they would like to sell or keep for personal consumption. For many people, pig options revolve around bacon and pork; some niches require a special kind of pig product. Here, you must use unique methods to meet this demand. Popular options include pork sausages, pork burgers, pork chops, and bacon.

Pigs are relatively cheap to maintain, especially compared to other animals such as cows. This is why farmers prefer to breed pigs for commercial meat because of their relatively low maintenance cost, coupled with their ability to produce a lot of meat quickly. Pigs, unlike most farm animals, can eat just about anything. They are omnivorous animals. These animals have a unique reproduction ability that will see your investment quickly reap the rewards. A sow can give birth twice a year to a litter of up to twelve piglets. Within a short period, you are almost guaranteed to double your pig-count on the farm.

While a cow needs pastures and fields where they can graze, pigs will more or less eat just about anything you throw at them. For instance, you could give them kitchen waste or even food scraps to eat. They are versatile animals that can be raised anywhere in the world on organic waste. Additionally, the feed to meat conversion ratio is more desirable than any other livestock. This means that the more food they eat, the more they grow and convert this food into flesh. Such factors combined make raising pigs a worthy investment.

Challenges of Keeping Pigs for Commercial Meat

Raising pigs for meat requires a decent amount of processing. For small scale farmers, this might present a significant challenge. For instance, in the United States, small scale farmers reported this challenge in Minnesota. Approximately 17% of all farmers reported adequate access to processing. Consider having sufficient access for processing your meat if you are planning to distribute it to a particular market directly. Alternatively, consider setting funds aside to cover processing fees for your hogs.

Another challenge that farmers encounter when keeping pigs for commercial meat is dealing with a pig carcass. Many farmers, both large- and small-scale, struggle to distribute pork, including the whole carcass. Capturing the full value of your hog will remain a constant challenge. In most markets, especially in the USA and Europe, pig carcass components, including byproducts, do not contribute to the overall earnings that a farmer receives. Here, you should sell pigs as a whole if the opportunity presents itself.

Raising Pigs for Compost

If you run a farm, one thing that you must deal with is manure. Raising pigs is a great way to help you turn waste into compost for your plants and garden. Compost, also known as "black gold," is beneficial as it adds nutrients and beneficial organisms to the soil. Furthermore, it is good for the overall environment, just like composting and recycling kitchen and yard waste.

Early farmers used to till the land with pig manure to allow it to decompose into critical nutrients for the next batch of crops. Today, this practice is uncommon as pig manure carries a host of harmful bacteria and parasites. Pig composting is one of the key reasons you should raise pigs on your farm.

How to Use Pig Manure for Compost

The key to effective composting is mixing the right ingredients at a high temperature. One way to comfortably work around this is by adding pig manure to a compost pile consisting of vegetable waste, dead leaves, weeds, and dried grass and allowing the mixture to decompose. Also consider heating the pile of compost as temperature and fertilizer go hand in hand. The temperature should be between 30-60 degrees Celsius. The heat will destroy unwanted living organisms, including seeds and potential weeds. And the heat helps the pile of manure turn into compost quickly.

One crucial aspect of composting involves aeration. Allow air to flow in the mixture for the pile to turn into compost. Frequently turning the mix using a rake, shovel, or pitchfork is a great way to increase air flow into the pile. Drive any of this farm equipment into the bottom of the pile and bring them to the top. Consider repeating this movement at least once every three weeks. The compost should be ready for use after approximately four months but the longer the compost stays, the richer it becomes.

Moisture is key to activating the compost. If the fertilizer is too dry, all the nutrients and micro-organisms living inside will die, failing to activate the compost effectively. Consider adding a fair degree of moisture into the pile. One way to quickly check for moisture in your compost is by putting your hand in it and squeezing. If you don't get a damp sponge-like feeling, then your pile is reasonably dry.

Challenges of Raising Pigs for Manure and Composting

If you do not heat the pile of pig manure and vegetable waste well or long enough, it will cause a rather unpleasant smell. Additionally, it might take even longer to break down and turn into compost. This is one challenge that farmers, especially small-scale farmers, encounter when turning pig manure into compost.

And excess moisture only causes a foul smell, flies, and creates a breeding ground for harmful bacteria and living organisms. This happens when a person adds fresh material such as vegetables and leaves without the right balance.

Keeping Pigs as Pets

Pigs are intelligent, engaging, and social animals. All these qualities combined make pigs one of the best animals to keep as pets. Pet pigs are also called "mini-pigs" or miniature pigs. Common breeds of pigs kept as pets include the Ossabaw Island pig. The number of mini pig owners is increasing with each passing year. For instance, Canada and the United States had over 200,000 mini pigs back in 1998. This figure has since skyrocketed to more than a million in recent years.

Rightly so, these animals are fun to be around—their average lifespan ranges from 10 to 15 years. Pig keepers should consider a few factors before keeping a hog as a pet.

Legal Considerations

While you may consider a pig as a pet, they are legally recognized as farm animals in most countries across the world. Fortunately, some states grant permits that allow residents to keep pigs as pets. You must observe the rules and regulations surrounding the domestication of these animals, depending on your country and location. For instance, Scotland does not allow residents to walk their pigs on a leash like a dog.

Check with your local authorities before keeping a pig as a pet. Additionally, keep all records, including vaccinations, medications, trips to the veterinary clinic, etc., to avoid legal complications.

What do pet pigs eat?

Just like cats and dogs, pigs have their dietary requirements, and this differs from other pets. When feeding a pet pig, it is essential to remember these animals have one of the best feed to meat ratio, which means they quickly grow with increased food consumption. To prevent obesity in your pet pig, consider feeding them with regulated commercial diets.

However, most pet pigs enjoy feeding on sow nuts, which are readily available from many farm suppliers. Consider giving the animal a handful every morning and every night, and. consider supplementing the diet with fruits and vegetables as pigs also enjoy these options. Please note that most countries do not advocate feeding pigs with any waste or scraps. In fact, many consider it illegal.

Last, your pet, just like us humans, requires a decent amount of water every day. The amount of water that a pig needs will vary with the size of the animal. For instance, a "mini-pig" or a miniature pig can drink up to five liters of water daily. But your pig will require access to fresh and clean water every day. Remember that pigs like to forage and will occasionally put their feet and body inside a water trough, making the water dirty. As a result, you might have to change the water several times a day to keep it fresh and clean.

Welfare

As mentioned above, pigs are intelligent animals. Their cognitive, physical, and social enrichment is a vital part of their well-being. Consider giving your pigs durable toys to play and forage with, and consider keeping them in pairs or groups for their social well-being.

Mini-pigs require decent housing and shelter. It should be dry, safe, ventilated, and well maintained. Fortunately, pigs are usually clean and restrict their toilet activities to one area. Consider giving your pigs a decent shelter to make a home. Also remember that young piglets are vulnerable, so consider keeping them in a warm and safe area for the first few weeks.

Challenges of Keeping Pigs as Pets

Pigs present several challenges to pet owners. First, there is no way to predict the extent to which the pig will grow. Most pig owners buy these animals when they are relatively young and small. Pigs can grow to enormous sizes, and as mentioned above, their food to meat ratio is relatively high. A pig can grow and weigh up to 450 kg, which makes it challenging to maintain as a pet. There are specific breeds such as the Ossabaw breed, Göttingen mini pigs, and Juliana pigs that do not grow to these astronomical sizes. But it is still somewhat hard to determine the extent to which the pigs will grow when you first get them.

Pigs require significant care. For instance, as they grow, they will need new housing or shelter because of the considerable increase in size. Second, mini pigs need oiling before they can go out in the sun because of their sensitive skin. Third, poor diet and nutrition can lead to seizures and arthritis, which are challenging to treat in pigs. They are also vulnerable to dog attacks. In many ways, these animals need extra care, attention, and time, which pet owners might not always have.

Pigs are naturally foragers and explorers. Their natural rooting behavior might destroy property, including household items such as furniture or outside items, including flowers and gardening equipment. If they are bored, their curious nature will lead them to explore neighboring environments. In the process, they might get lost or hurt if they encounter animals such as dogs.

Sows (female pigs) will come into heat a few weeks after they are born, and this process will continue every three weeks. If they have children, sows become aggressive and territorial. The same goes for the boars. Aggressive behavior can lead to injuries or the destruction of property. Consider a friendly and calm demeanor when handling these animals to reduce any chances of anxiety or aggressive behavior.

Most of these pig challenges can be avoided with a more profound understanding of the animal. Pigs are fun to be around and have proven to be loyal companions. In-depth knowledge of these animals will help you avoid most of these challenges in your quest to become a mini pig owner.

Chapter 2: Choosing the Right Breed

Pigs are intelligent animals. They are quite beneficial to have around and are considered social animals. They are all omnivores, meaning they feed on plants, animals, and almost everything else. Domesticated pigs are raised for commercial purposes to produce pork, ham, or bacon. Other pigs are kept as pets, such as Kune Kunes.

There are different kinds of pigs available. You can pick either male pigs, commonly called *boars*, or females, known as *sows*. These pigs come in many colors, such as brown, white, tan, red, gold, ginger, cream, and black. You will need to choose whether you want all sows, or a mixture of sows and boars, depending on your commercial or domestic needs and capabilities. This can be challenging, but you can pick whatever suits you best using the list below.

Different Breeds of Pigs

Pigs come in many shapes, sizes, and colors. This can be overwhelming for any farmer when they want to make the best purchase. The list below will help you get to know the different types of pigs, the differences, and the ease of rearing each one of them.

The main types of pigs are commercial and heritage pigs. Commercial pigs are reared in factories in large numbers. The primary purpose of raising these pigs is to provide meat. They require a lot of feed and are not as fat compared to heritage pigs.

Heritage pig breeds are the best option for small scale farmers. They are easy to rear and provide delicious meat. They are relatively easy to manage as they feed on pasture.

Here are the best breeds to rear in your backyard:

1. Wooly Mangalica

The Wooly Mangalica is famous for its wooly coat; no other pig fosters this feature. They come highly recommended by small-scale farmers. They produce high quality and tasty meat. Their meat is tender and retains delicious fat juices. It provides fantastic bacon.

Pros

- They are low maintenance
- They have manageable temperaments
- They don't rely heavily on protein
- They can adapt quickly to the winter season
- They have high returns

Cons

- They produce a lot of fat, which can be overwhelming

2. Red Wattle

The Red Wattle is one of the most amiable pigs alive. They have a humble demeanor, which makes them a great companion. They are red with spots across their body. They can be quite heavy and large. Why should you buy this pig?

Pros

- They have a high growth rate

- The meat is tender, lean, and non-fatty

- The sows are very motherly, reducing your work significantly

- They have a high birth rate

The Red Wattle is a great pig to rear for a first-time farmer. They are straightforward to manage and are non-aggressive. They are very friendly and will give you an easy time when breeding. They also help the soil by foraging. They are great in small confinements, so no need to expand your pen. They can go up to 1,000 pounds, which can bring outstanding returns after a few months.

3. Gloucestershire Old Spots Pigs

This pig is white with large black spots across its body. It is known for its docility and intelligence.

Pros

- High maternal instincts

- High birth rate

- They are best suited outdoors

- High-quality meat

4. Kune Kune

Kune Kune is known for its docile nature, sweet meat, and excellent temperament. They are medium sized and are great when confined. Why should you buy this pig?

Pros

- Their smell is not overwhelming

- They are calm and quiet

- They make great crossbreeds

Cons

- They do not have fur, so they need shelter when it rains
- They need particular feed

5. Chester White

The Chester White is the most common pig in most homesteads. Here are some of the reasons why farmers like them:

Pros

- They have extensive life spans
- The sows are very motherly
- They are bulky and muscular
- They require minimal maintenance

6. American Yorkshire Pig

The American Yorkshire pig is a popular member of different homesteads. The pretty pink skin is common all over farms in many locations. Here are the reasons you should have one.

Pros

- They have a high growth rate
- They have a high birth rate
- They are muscular
- They are affordable to rear
- They have tasty meat
- The sows are incredibly motherly, reducing your monitoring rounds

7. Berkshire Pig

These are small black pigs with white socks, white tip on tail, and prick ears. The Berkshire pig is a popular choice among small scale farmers, and they are the oldest breed. Why should you buy a Berkshire Pig:

Pros

- They have very delicious meat
- They are active foragers
- They have a high growth rate
- They are very friendly

8. Large Black Pig

They are also known as the Devon or Cornwall. They tend to have an elongated form. Most small-scale farmers buy them because:

- They are easy to manage
- They are great producers of bacon
- They are adaptable
- They are resistant to sunburn

9. Hampshire Pig

The Hampshire pig is easily identifiable with the white belt on its shoulders and front legs. They have large ears. They are very active and are known for their erect ears.

Pros

- They have a high growth rate
- They have a high birth rate
- They are generally large
- They have good temperament
- The sows have a high maternal instinct

Cons

- They do not weigh as much compared to other pig breeds
- They have smaller hams

10. Landrace

It's a great pig for rearing indoors or even outdoors. The pig's carcass is exceptional for bacon and pork. Landrace has white skin with black hair. It also has drooping ears with a slight slant forward. They have long middle forequarters.

Pros

- They have excellent ham development
- Sows have a high birth rate
- The piglets have a high growth rate
- High-quality lean meat
- It's ideal for crossbreeding

Cons

- They are prone to sunburn due to the coat and skin color

11. Duroc

The Duroc is usually called Red Hog. It has a large frame with small droopy ears. It's quite a muscular pig with medium length. The head and the neck are light in complexion. Duroc has hard skin with a solid red color.

Pros

- They can survive extreme temperatures
- Succulent flesh with a lot of muscles
- They are extremely friendly

Cons

- They take time to mature

12. Large White

It is well-developed for the outdoors. It is a long, large pig with white skin, white hair, and long ears that stick up.

Pros

- They can withstand extreme weather
- They have high birth rates
- They have high milk production
- The sows have a high maternal instinct
- Prone to sunburn due to lack of pigmentation

Cons

- Their hams are of less quality.

How to Select the Best Breed

Selecting the correct breeding stock for your farm is crucial for your farm's success. It is essential to consider the litter growth, size, and feed efficiency before making any purchase. Several traits of a pig should also be considered, such as long life, adaptability to different housing and temperature, carcass quality, resistance to diseases, and ease of rebreeding.

If you are a first-time farmer, remember these different factors. The availability of food supply means dealing with pig output, local beliefs (religion), availability of the pig breed, local requirements, local and global market conditions, and the local diseases prone to pigs. These factors are instrumental in guiding the type of pig you will select and the sustainability.

These steps will help you in the selection process:

Why Do You Want to Raise Pigs?

There are several reasons farmers raise pigs. This could be for personal consumption, for sale, as a pet, or even for breeding. The reason as to why you are raising pigs changes the requirements you will have. Pigs intended for sale will require a more routine structure with high maintenance from the farmer. Pigs intended to be petted will need a less monitored environment.

How Big Are Your Facilities?

Small scale pig farmers are at an advantage compared to those having a large farm. This will be easier for maintenance. This is a significant element of pig rearing.

What Are Your Preferences?

Pick pigs you like, whether you want spotty ones, brown, white, black or prefer small, medium, or large. There are many friendly pigs available in the market.

What Are Your Capabilities?

Large pigs require a lot of work. If you are active and free, you can choose the large pigs. Choose small pigs if you do not have as much dedicated time, especially if you are starting pig farming. This will enable you to grow at your own pace, acquiring knowledge and experience.

After answering the above questions, you can easily identify the next factors.

Select from A Proper Farm

Pig breeders are very common, and it can be a daunting task to find the right farm to buy your pigs. The quality of the breed is affected by the environs. An adequate farm should manage its breeds with a high level of cleanliness and pre-planned programs. The lifespan of a particular pig that is confined can stretch up to ten years. This depends on its management and genetic composition.

Pigs have different character traits that are easily identifiable. You can rate the performance of the breed by checking on the maternal ability. The maternal pig should be able to nurse the piglets to the weaning stage, check on the number of piglets, and the rate of weight gain.

A good breeder will not only sell the pigs to you, but they will follow up after the sale. They will answer any queries and give more information regarding the pigs. Some will even offer free delivery to your proposed location.

Choose Registered Pigs

Always select registered pigs, as this will ensure that you get the quality purported by the breeder. Without registration, it will be difficult to gauge the different aspects of the pig. The ear-notches or tags easily identify a pedigree pig.

Selecting the best breed is easy once you have established the traits. The following are vital things you should check before settling for any purchase.

Check the Characteristics of the Best Breeds

Before buying any swine, make sure that the pigs are of high standard. Generally, you can gauge their health by checking their alertness; their eyes should be bright, and they should show ease of movement. You can also check how quickly they devour food and whether their ribs are visible. Be able to check whether the pig is active or dull. A malnourished pig will be dull and withdrawn.

Check on the temperament of the pig. Do not choose an aggressive or timid pig. Aggressive pigs are not suitable for rearing, especially for a first-time farmer. Go for pigs that are young as opposed to older pigs; buy pigs about ten weeks old.

Body Features

The neck should be longer than average. This will make the shoulders appear to have a downward slope. When standing, the pig should appear to have slanted forearms.

The pastern is the location between the pig's hoof and the joint with the dewclaws. This area should have a gentle forward slope. The toes of all the legs should be moderately large.

Check on the buttocks as well. This is called the *rump*. The top line should appear flat-like, with the tail fixed high on it. The hind legs should be straight but curved after the knee joint.

The hock joint is located at the "heel" of the foot. This is an important area to be wary of before purchasing. Check on the shape or form of the hock joint to establish if it is healthy.

Also check on the teats of the pig. A healthy pig will have well-spaced breasts that are long and slender. Pigs have almost 32 teats running parallel on the underside from the groin to the chest. The average pig will have 10-14 pairs of teats projecting milk. The number of teats is essential, as it will dictate how many piglets it can feed at once.

What to Consider

Inspecting a pig before a purchase is extremely important. First check the teats of the pigs. If they do not project outwards from the skin, then the mother will not be able to feed the piglets, as the mammary glands will dry off after birth, becoming useless. The pigs with extra teats are also not a good buy; the teats will not deliver milk after birth.

Check the report the farm has on the different pigs. Note the birth rate of the pig, the maternal performance, growth rate of the sows, and the presence of genetic deformities, if any. Any mother that weans less than ten piglets at a time should not be bought. Check on the rate of mastitis in the sows. This is an infection that occurs in the mammary glands of the mother pig. Also, check for metritis, an infection of the uterus, and agalactia, which is a lack of milk production.

When purchasing the pig, go with someone with a lot more experience in pig rearing. They will help you identify the best breeders and pigs for breeding. An experienced breeder will easily spot defects in their pigs. Remember, the pig price is an important factor to consider. The price tends to be different from one breeder to the next. Younger pigs are generally less expensive, whereas boars and sows are more expensive because they have proven to be fertile.

It is essential to check if they have been vaccinated against any diseases. Pigs rarely have routine medication, but there must be basic injections against common pig diseases such as Erysipelas. Obtain all the registration documents from the breeder. You will need them as proof of vaccination.

Selecting Pigs Intended for Cross-Breeding

If you are a small-scale pig keeper looking to upgrade your existing stock, you must be vigilant in the selection process. Important factors to consider when crossbreeding pigs include cost and time. The most crucial factor is that they do not lower the standards of the existing stock or introduce diseases. You must consult your veterinary doctor before embarking on any purchase.

Get information about the disease history of the pigs and the current health status. Examine the health reports of the pigs and get to know a detailed medical history of the animals.

Remember the market acceptability, the genetics, availability, and the quality of the incoming pigs to your farm.

Chapter 3: Housing, Fencing, and Facilities

During the sunny days, when the nights are short and the days are hot, pigs may sleep out under the sun. Regardless, you will need to provide housing and accommodation. Before purchasing your pigs, make sure there is a dry and cool house, safe from the threats of harsh temperatures and other animals. For their overall wellbeing and productivity, these animals require adequate space, and access to water and food.

There are many pig houses on the market, and you have many options to choose from. Failure to build the proper housing for your pigs can lead to severe problems that affect your pig's overall wellbeing and productivity. When housing pigs, carefully consider the following factors.

The Environment and Site Location

The location in which you erect the pig's housing should be elevated or slightly raised. Such a location is necessary to avoid flooding when it rains. And the site should be protected from the sun to provide shade. The area should be cool, with fresh air to keep the pigs cool.

Temperature

As mentioned, high temperatures make pigs uncomfortable as they cannot sweat and cool their bodies. To achieve the best productivity from your pigs, consider observing a specific temperature range. For instance, the most favorable temperature for newborn piglets ranges between 27 C and 35 C, but temperatures above 27 C are deemed unfavorable for most pig breeds.

Pigs can tolerate cold temperatures, but they are not comfortable in drafty areas. A drafty area is an enclosed space in an open area characterized by a lot of currents, usually of cold air. Consider having the housing location moved to a cool area free from winds or currents of cold air. If such a location is not an option, it would be best to check where the drafts are coming from and put a stop to them.

Hygiene

The overall hygiene of the house will affect the pig's health and productivity. Many diseases are caused by unsanitary conditions, which create a suitable environment for the growth of harmful living organisms. These micro-organisms inhabit the pig's gut causing stunted growth and problems with manure.

Water and Drainage

Freshwater supply is essential for raising pigs. Consider having a year-round supply of potable water for animal consumption and sanitization. Water will come in handy when diluting lagoons or putting out fires. Where groundwater is not sufficient, consider using additional sources such as ponds and community water systems.

If the pig house is in an area with significant rainfall or snow, think about constructing a slope or a runoff around the house to reduce the amount of water near the location. Runoff water can be contaminated, jeopardizing the health of your hogs. Additionally, high water tables impact the construction of buildings and manure storage.

Manure Management

When selecting a site for raising pigs, consider one with adequate space for manure management. Depending on where you live, there will be different guidelines on the basic acreage required based on the nitrogen requirements for growing crops. However, the location you raise your pigs must be large enough for manure spreading. Avoid steep or high areas that could lead to manure runoffs, causing water and land pollution to adjacent environs.

Consider a rectangular pit measuring 10' x 8' x 6'. For 50-70 fully grown pigs, this pit will take approximately five months to fill.

Security and Safety

Pig safety and security is an essential factor when it comes to site location. Remember that there are issues of theft and vandalism across the world. Also, visitors can infect animals with life-threatening diseases, so consider an area with limited human access to control diseases while reducing interference with other farm operations.

Feeding and Drinking Area

Pigs should have these areas built systematically, preferably in a line, within the structure. It is advisable to have each pig have its own feeder but a general drinking area they can all share. The recommended size of the feeding trough should measure approximately 12" x 12" x 6". Although these measurements are standard, younger pigs might not require such large feeding areas.

Space Requirements

As raising pigs is a worthwhile investment, it would be wise of you to remember that they might double in size after a relatively short time. Different animals require different housing facilities. The following are housing suggestions for different pigs.

Fattening Pigs

The fattening phase of a pig commences as soon as the piglets start maturing (usually between weeks 8 and 15). This period does not stop until the pigs are brought to slaughter after they attain a minimum weight of 85 kg to 170 kg. For such pigs, consider a minimum space of 0.5 sqm (5 square feet) to 1 sqm (10 square feet) for each pig. This will give you adequate space for feeding, stabling, and anti-stress solutions.

Consider using a housing/spacing model with a flat solid floor made from concrete, hard soil, or cement. The floor should be slightly inclined to make it easier to clean with fresh water.

Pregnant Sows

Pregnant sows require a quiet and peaceful environment. Remember that the house should be free from all types of elements that could stress these animals, such as temperature, ventilation, hygiene, and noise. With that said, every pregnant sow requires at least 1.5 (approx. 16 sq. f) sqm to 2.0 sqm. In hot climates, consider keeping sows in groups of two or three.

Lactating Sows

There are many factors regarding productivity and efficiency that affect sows. One of them is inadequate housing and feeding programs. Lactating sows need to be fed more than twice a day for the best results. The importance of a proper house in removing wet and spoiled feed from the feeders should not be overlooked. Additionally, these animals need a quiet environment.

Therefore, it is advisable to use individual pens. These pens should have provisions for farrowing pans, cooling, heating a piglet nest, and a starter feed for piglets. The recommended housing size for each sow is approximately six square meters.

Weaner Piglets

Weaner piglets are usually small but grow to about 25 kg in six to seven weeks. Each piglet will require about 0.3 to 0.5 sqm. The floor housing should be made of concrete to make it easier to maintain or clean. It should not be polished to avoid slipping. Just like the other pens, the floor should be slightly inclined to facilitate cleaning with water.

Breeding Boars

Housing requirements for breeding boars are often overlooked. If the conditions are not optimum for these animals, they will "break down," limiting their overall output.

Breeding boars require a strong and well-insulated pen for sleeping and feeding. Breeding boars are usually kept alone and are prone to temperature variations. And mature boars have little fat cover to insulate them when it is cold. In the winter seasons, consider giving these animals increased bedding to provide them with extra warmth.

Areas with high temperatures also affect a boar's performance. Libido is usually affected before there is an impact on sperm quality. If prolonged high temperature occurs, sperm quality can be affected for approximately six to eight weeks. All these factors suggest that housing for breeding boars is crucial to their productivity and overall performance.

The floor housing for the boars should be made from cement to make it easier to clean. It shouldn't be polished because the pigs will often slip, risking serious injuries.

The size of the pen should be at least seven to eight sqm (3 x 3 or 2.3 x 3). The gates and overall structure of the pens should be strong to prevent the boars from escaping. When they are in heat, they might find ways of escaping the pen to secure a mate.

Building Plans for a Good Pig House/Shed

As a small-scale farmer, there are several good options you should consider for housing your pigs. First, you must consider the accommodation type required for the different classes of pigs.

Construction Plans for a Single Pig

Consider using locally available materials. Not only are local materials cost-effective, but you will have an easier time assembling these materials.

- The floor of the house/pen should be at least 9 sqm (3 m x 3 m)

- The floor of the house should be raised at least 0.6 m (1.9685 feet/ 60 cm)

- Consider spacing the floorboards (at least 2 cm).

- The roof should be made from water-resistant materials; should be water or rainproof.

- The house should be constructed so it shades sunlight to protect the pigs. The house could have provisions to allow a little sunlight in the house, but there should always be shade in the house.

Construction Plans for a Pen Housing Sows

The smallest unit you can build is a pen housing a sow and her piglets. These pens can be used for a sow and her litter, two litters of weaned piglets, about four gestating sows, nine piglets, or one boar.

Construction Plans

- Length- 4 meters with 1.4 meters allocated for manure management

- Width- 2.7 meters

- Height-3.4 meters (highest) or 1.1 meters (lowest)

- 60 cm raised off the ground. You can build the floor using either cement, wooden poles, or wooden slates and bricks.

- Two troughs (Although with one boar or fattening pigs, consider using one)

- Most of the area should be allocated feeding; creep management

- There area should be slightly raised to allow for drainage when cleaning with water

Fencing Plans

Pigs can pose credible challenges when it comes to fencing. As mentioned above, these animals are intelligent and curious by nature. That means they will occasionally look for weak areas in the fencing system as they try to break free and explore other areas. Having a sound perimeter is important as you will be avoiding liability problems with hogs, especially when they run to neighboring areas to wreak havoc.

Should you build a permanent structure to serve you for the foreseeable future, then the best course of action will be to use a medium grilled rolled wire fence. This option is great as this material is tough and can withstand efforts from the pigs to cut loose.

Pigs usually escape through the bottom of the fence. There is no need to build the fence over four feet tall (48 inches). If it is within your budget, consider adding electricity inside the fence. Should the pigs come too close, the electric shock will quickly have them retreating. Keep checking the state of the electric fence as certain items could disrupt the flow of the current, risking the pigs escaping.

If electricity is not an option, then the bottom wires should be meshed closely together to prevent both mature and baby pigs from escaping.

Effects of Bad Housing

Parasitic Infection

Failure to erect proper housing for the pigs can lead to the contraction of diseases and infections. As a pig keeper, consider providing an optimal environment necessary for the safety of the animal, reducing the chances of hospitalization by disease-causing agents. For instance, sows may contract mastitis (which is characterized by a reduction in milk production, loss of appetite, and high body temperature) if the housing is wet and unhygienic. Furthermore, poor housing can lead to the spread of contagious diseases to both pigs and humans.

Economic Losses

The housing can negatively affect your investment. For instance, if the house is not strong enough, the pigs will escape because of their curious nature. Also, poor housing will affect the production of meat negatively as conditions will not be favorable for developing the animals, and may lead to stunted growth - not desirable for the overall production of meat.

Chapter 4: Pig Behavior and Handling

Gaining a good understanding of how a pig behaves is vital for ensuring the animal meets its daily needs. Natural behavior can be observed when it's in its natural habitat or even in the wild. A pig's performance is altered depending on the location and many other factors. Here we outline the various behaviors to expect. This will significantly affect how you handle a pig and its production quality. Once you gain a proper understanding of how a pig behaves, you can:

- Facilitate animal handling

- Reduce stress and frustration

- Reduce risk to the handler

- Reduce loss due to fatigue, injuries and bruising

Of course, it much easier to handle calm pigs than agitated or stressed ones! If a handler uses basic handling practices, the pigs will be less likely to become agitated. The handler should take into account:

- Point of balance
- Fight zone
- Senses

The Fight Zone

This is the area a pig considers as its individual space. Pigs actively try to maintain a certain distance between the handler and themselves. The distance differs from one pig to the next. The more threatening the handler appears to be, the more distance the pig requires. When a handler becomes too frightening, the pig gets defensive, and their body language immediately changes. As a handler, you must recognize the cues from stressed pigs and establish more distance or back off until they are calm again.

Point of Balance

The pig uses this to gauge the direction they should take when they are moving away from the handler. The point of balance is usually located at the shoulder but adjusts depending on the environment. Different conditions spark different reactions from the pigs. To achieve optimum results, the handler must work ahead of the pigs. For example, if a handler wants to get the pigs through the gates, they must avoid stroking the pig's rear while standing in front. The handlers should not block, move, or interfere with the pigs from the front position. Pigs tend to balk when coerced to move past people.

Sense of Hearing

A pig utilizes their sense of smell and hearing to situate itself in different environments. They use their sight to complement the two senses. They have a blind spot that does not allow them to see the rear; the eyes are on the sides, giving them 310 degrees coverage. Pigs have an uncanny ability to spot any threat or pressure. They always make sure their handlers are within their line of sight, and they also use their hearing to track the movement of people they cannot see. A handler must know the vision span of pigs to facilitate their movement effectively. Their sense of touch is also essential.

Pig Behavior

You can establish what a pig pays attention to by observing their ears, head, eyes, and body language. Handlers should note the directions pigs are looking, how they twist their bodies, turn their heads, and position their ears. Pigs tend to track their handlers even more when they feel threatened. Pigs will become more stressed in confined areas. The pressure from the handler during this time will make the pigs draw closer as opposed to pulling away. When they become agitated, they lie in a group and refuse to move. The body language of pigs change as they become more excited.

Releasing Pressure

This is any action intended to reduce the level of frustration of a pig. It involves giving the pigs a lot of time and space. Here are some ways of reducing pressure:

- Step back and avoid constant contact with the pigs
- Pause and allow the pigs to move away
- Ease your body language to make the pigs feel safe
- Allow the pigs to circle past you
- Stop making too much noise
- Look away from the pigs
- Reduce the group size—this depends on the size, environment, door, and the aisle.

Pigs can effectively communicate their emotions through their heads, ears, eyes, and body movements. Here are signs that the pigs are fearful when moving them:

Calm Pigs

Calm pigs will have these qualities:

- Ability to maintain a safe distance from the handler to relieve pressure

- Heads and ears are usually low, and the body is relaxed

- Attention is usually directed forward

- Vocalization is very minimal and in low tones

Mild Stressed Pigs

Here are reasons/signs that your pig is showing mild fear:

- A handler is getting too close to the pigs and not giving them enough release from pressure

- The heads and ears are always rising

- The pigs will move away but fix their attention on the handler

- The fighting zone is expanding

- The pigs will increase their speed briefly

- Releasing pressure from the pig will calm them

- If you continuously sustain the pressure, they become fearful

Defensiveness in Pigs

Here are reasons/signs that a pig is experiencing heightened fear:

- The handler is administering too much pressure and is getting too close

- Their full attention is on the handler

- The pig adopts different tactics as opposed to moving away—stopping, backing up, or turning back

- The pigs shut down and refuse to move, showing signs of fatigue

- Releasing the pressure will calm the pig down with time

- Escalating the pressure will make the pig escalate their tactics

- They tend to bunch up and refuse to separate

Extreme Defensiveness

The signs that a pig is experiencing intense fear:

- Panic

- High pitched vocalization

- Willing to run over the handler bunching up and difficult to separate

Herd Behavior and Group Patterns

Pigs seek solace in one another for protection. The extent to which pigs associate with one another depends on their fear level, their attention, and the available space.

Flowing Herd Behavior

This is what occurs when pigs move together. The flowing movement occurs when:

- Pigs are drawn to the movement of other pigs

- Calm pig response

- The attention is towards moving and staying with the herd

- Movement of front animals encourages movement from the rest

- Animals are loosely spaced

- The handler is not coercing movement from the pigs. The pigs are clear from obstructions

Disrupting Flow

The movement and distractions ahead or from the sides can take the pigs' attention, preventing them from moving. Factors like excessive noise, pressure, and crowding will also stop the movement. These changes can affect the pigs' movement:

- Footing/traction
- Temperature
- Lighting
- Floor surface

Other factors that may affect the pig's movement:

- People on their path
- Drafts or wind
- A beam of light shining through a crack
- Equipment, trash, or objects in the path
- Loud or sudden noises or activities
- Water puddles
- Shiny or reflective objects
- Change in color of equipment
- Moving or flapping objects
- Other animals
- Change in the height of the flooring

Handlers who can read these signs with ease keep their pigs calm by giving them space and time. Take time to remove all distractions from the environment before buying a new breed. Pay attention to the body language of the pigs. When the pigs are getting more afraid, the handler needs to release the pressure.

Most handlers get agitated when transporting and unloading the pigs, because of the new personnel that will receive, count, tattoo, and move the pigs. It is vital that the transporter minimizes the contact with the pigs, give them ample space and time to get into the truck.

Bunch Herd Behavior

This occurs when pigs remain still when the group is stopped. Bunching is a defensive response by pigs to stop movement, especially during ear tagging or vaccination. It is caused by anything that traps, crowds, stops, or confuses the pigs. It occurs when the pigs are facing away from the handler. They tend to be closely paced and listen intently.

You can easily identify this early by checking on the ears or crowding of the group. Pigs will opt to stay in a bunch as opposed to leaving the bunch to steer away from the handler. When a handler increases pressure or aggressiveness, the pigs will tighten the bunch.

Handler's Bubble

The handler's bubble can also be regarded as the *fight zone* for handlers. The bubble takes up real space that leads to crowding. It changes depending on the pig's level of fear or the handler's pressure. It acts as a real barrier that moves with the handler.

Pigs move according to the arc of the bubble. Handlers can note the movement of the pigs to actualize the arc of the bubble, using this information to direct the pigs properly. Small pigs tend to pile away to get away from the bubble. Large pigs hold still within the bubble. You can use large animals to face a particular direction so that the rest can follow.

Rooting Behavior

This is where the pig uses its snout to push something repeatedly. The pigs root to find food like truffles, grubs, and roots. Rooting is regarded as an exploratory behavior need. This is a great activity, especially if you need your land to be cultivated or weeded; however, it can pose a challenge to those with gardens. A nose ring is inserted on the septum to prevent this behavior.

Lack of proper feeding regiments increases the frequency of rooting. The different levels of rooting depend on the nutritional needs of the pigs. On average, the sow spends at least a quarter of its life rooting. This can be an advantage to those with larger tracts of land needing cultivation.

If you want to reduce rooting, you can opt to plant root crops on the land, but this is not the best alternative compared to nose rings. You can use edible enrichments to prevent damage to the paddock. Sows prefer branches and peats as rooting materials.

Environmental Enrichment

This refers to providing pigs an opportunity to root, play, and investigate its environs to make it more comfortable. This is usually seen when you give pigs a long straw, and they play with it then store it for later use. You must implement this with regard to the requirements of the pigs. Enrichment can stimulate foraging if used appropriately. Through it, piglets tend to rise high in the social status of the pen. You can identify the need for enriching by spotting injuries on the neck, ears, and head of the pig.

Pigs usually use rooting behavior as a way to find food and obtain nutritional balance. The pigs generally use their snout and mouth to root. Even without the reward of food, they will root. Farm pigs spend a lot of their time investigating and manipulating the environs – an excellent way of establishing the health status of the animals. Failure to provide a distraction to keep the pigs occupied can lead to tail biting.

Enrichment highly affects weaners as opposed to the much older pigs. All pigs still prefer having a stimulant that will draw them away from harming each other.

Maternal Behavior

There is a recurring behavior among sows that undergo isolation, community integration, and living. Farrowing the environment greatly affects the sows. Female pigs need to construct their own nest and farrow the environs; this is done most often when the sow is in distress.

Isolation

This stage lasts two days before giving birth to the first piglet. The sow tends to isolate itself from the group and looks for a nest. The sow can walk up to six kilometers investigating the environs to find the perfect spot. Sows choose areas far from the group, as well as sloping ground. She constructs the nest using straw and makes sure that the walls of the nest are strong.

Nest Building

This process occurs in stages as the sow must check on various factors before settling on the new area. The sow must make sure the spot is about four inches deep before proper construction. Then she looks for grass, leaves, and roots to line the nest for comfort. She puts large branches over the nest and covers with light materials to form a roof.

Farrowing

This is done after building the nest. The sow is usually very passive during the process. She sniffs and investigates the piglets that are born. The sow barely gets up to help the piglets from their membrane. The umbilical cord detaches itself when the piglet moves to the udder. The sow's inactivity is due to the numerous piglets it has birthed, but it usually regains its energy after two days of rest. It's a great adaptation that prevents the sow from crushing its newborn.

Nest Occupation

This occurs a week after farrowing. The maternal instincts of the sow dictate the nursing routine. The sow can initiate by lying on its side or by the squealing piglets. The sow grunts a lot during this period. As the grunts become more rapid, the piglets become quiet and continue to suckle. This is followed by piglets butting and nosing at the udder. Some piglets detach themselves and go on to sleep or play. The sow can end the nursing by standing up or rolling over.

Social Integration

The piglets are not introduced to the rest of the herd until they are one week old. In the first two days, the sow does not eat as much as before, but as time goes by, the sow moves farther away from the nest and eventually re-joins the herd. The litter takes a few more days and then joins the herd as well. The sow introduces its offspring to the herd, establishing their relation immediately. In the first seven days, the litter maintains proximity to the sow. The litter gradually starts interacting with other piglets in the herd. The litter shouldn't be integrated with the rest of the herd until it's at least fourteen days old.

Weaning

The frequency of nursing decreases after the first week. Piglets begin to wean four weeks after birth. In eight weeks, the piglet only consumes solid food in its diet. Different litters have different weaning stages, but it usually ranges from eight to seventeen weeks postpartum.

Mixing and Fighting

Once pigs are mixed, they go through a phase to establish social relationships. Some pigs dominate, while others become subordinate. It is crucial to be certain that the pen is socially stable. Establishing social relationship requires some pigs to fight. Pigs that do not fight are consequentially subordinate.

During these fights, the pigs do not eat. They decrease in weight significantly (the newly weaned pigs are not affected as they do not eat as much as the others.) The subordinates suffer the most as they do not feed as much as they would like. The old pigs, which are reserved when it comes to eating, tend to experience significant weight loss due to the disruption.

The size and age of the pigs determine the effect of the fight. The larger the pig, the more damage it causes. It is vital to avoid putting large pigs together as they can cause irreversible damage and injuries. If you spot a smaller pig being harassed, it is essential to relocate it to another pen.

Pig Handling

People handle pigs for various reasons, from medicating, transportation, weaning, or even birthing. Animals appropriately handled are gentler and more productive. Rough handling can cause lower production. Therefore, the persona must manage the pigs not to perform painful procedures as it may hinder the production.

Animal welfare has a lot to do with the way the pigs are handled. If the pig is improperly managed, it is induced with stress and fear, which can affect the quality of meat. It may also reduce the safety of the pig and the handler. Meat from a pig improperly handled tends to be pale or exudative. Proper handling can increase animal welfare, the quality of meat, and safety.

For an outdoor system, pig handling and care will require a lot of observation. Unlike indoor systems kept at a specific temperature, the outdoors offers a different experience to the pigs. It is, therefore, essential to note this will affect the behavior.

A stock person must develop a routine checkup on all pigs daily. Inspect the animals by walking through them gently. This is a vital exercise to detect animals that are sick or lame. Petting the pig through friendly stroking is also a significant factor to consider as it will help the pig gain more trust. It is also essential to check the drinkers.

Following are best practices for proper handling of pigs.

Handlers

It is not an easy task to handle pigs, for both the handler and the pigs. Being gentle and patient can ease the process by reducing the stress levels. Always remember that despite the high IQ of pigs, they do not fully understand what you want them to do. When you need to move them, it will be much easier if they are calm than excited. As a handler, you must move slowly and quietly so as not to disturb the pigs.

A handler should familiarize themselves with the pigs first. New handlers are not recommended, especially when moving the pigs. You are also required not to rush or yell at the pigs. It can be frustrating to move pigs as they may not be in the mood, but do not allow this to get to you. Practicing patience will bring more positive results. Never be quick to use aggressive methods simply because the pigs want to explore the environment.

Handling Tools

Handling equipment is used to provide barriers and stimuli, such as physical barriers, visual barriers, visual stimuli, and auditory stimuli. Several farm tools are friendly to pigs and may pose no danger or harm to them.

Using a nylon flag, cape, plastic ribbon, or sorting boards to move pigs or give them direction is highly recommended. Handlers should never use electric prods. These will make the pigs more aggressive and induce stress, therefore, affecting the quality of meat. Sorting boards are more effective when moving pigs.

Prodding animals is not recommended as it causes fear and stress. The electric prod raises the temperature of the pigs and the heart rate. Never prod a pig in the eyes, testicles, anus, or nose. These are extremely sensitive areas that may cause fatalities or health issues.

Here is a detailed view of the acceptable equipment mentioned above:

Nylon Flag

This is excellent equipment to stimulate pigs visually. The nylon flag is especially effective amongst large pigs. It is used to block the optical path of a pig or get its attention.

Matador's Cape (Witch's Cape)

The cape is useful in acting as a visual barrier with all pigs. It creates an illusion that the pig has reached a dead end.

Plastic Ribbons on a Stick

These provide visual stimulation when flapped or waved. It can create a proper distraction to move the pig in the correct direction.

Plastic Rattle

The rattle is quite a useful tool in providing auditory, visual, and physical stimuli. As a handler, you can also improvise and use shaker cans or bottles. The noise shouldn't be too loud and continuous, as this will inhibit the movement of pigs. Short spurts are quite effective in controlling the pigs.

Rattle paddles are also an efficient way of pig handling. Do not raise them above the shoulder when tapping the animals. The hit should be very gentle to prevent frightening the pigs. A simple touch of the pig with a rattle draws its attention. Pigs tend to move towards the paddle and brace it.

Avoid repeated contact and noise as they will prevent the pigs from moving. Paddles are very efficient in providing the pigs with visual aids. Do not move the paddle too much as this may stimulate the pigs negatively.

Sorting Board

This is the most versatile tool available on the farm. It is also known as a sorting panel that comes either as a single panel or bifold. The sorting board can be used as a visual aid or a physical barrier.

Electric Prod

This tool is not recommended during pig handling. There are cases where there are strict guidelines provided that may require its usage. There may be a situation whereby pigs are in a bunch at a doorway, and the electric prod may be needed to move them on.

When you shock the lead pig, it will jump and pave the way for the rest. Shocking the lead pig does not necessarily mean that the other pigs will move in the intended direction. The pig that follows may be scared and retreat to prevent being shocked. In this instance, do not shock all the pigs; simply give them time. After the pig realizes the lead pig is unharmed, the pigs will follow and enter the pen.

Using the prod is the last resort when all other tools have failed and should be put away immediately.

Mixing Pigs

When transporting pigs to a new pen, you must be very meticulous. Be sure the pen is not overcrowded, poorly ventilated, or fostering broken or sharp equipment. Mix all pigs simultaneously in a completely new pen. Mixing them at different times may cause the newcomers being beaten. It is advisable to mix many pigs at the same time, as opposed to a few pigs. The latter will also result in a lot of fighting.

Make sure the pen you have built has an escape route. This is a safety measure when a fight breaks out in pen. It is also not recommended that you group large pigs into standard weight pens.

As a handler, it is essential to know the signs of a stressed pig. You can easily tell if a pig is under duress if it has blotchy skin, stiffness, muscle tremors, reluctance to move, squealing, and panting. These indicators are useful in establishing the comfort of a pig and change to better tactics.

Training Animals

Pigs need to be trained to foster their safety and that of handlers. Pigs should be accustomed to handling to minimize stress. Pig handling occurs at different stages during the pig's stay. Handlers may need to clean the pen, showing and preparation, transportation, movement in the environment, and husbandry procedures. These activities will require a lot of handling that may stimulate the pigs negatively or positively. It is, therefore, vital to set up a routine that will help the pigs accustom. Routines will train the animals efficiently and help them acquire good habits.

Protective Equipment

To determine what equipment you will need, you can assess the tasks in loading, transporting, and unloading the pigs. It is essential to note down the injuries you may encounter during the process of protecting yourself. The minimum equipment a handler should have is a sorting board and safety boots. Handlers who travel inside the truck with the pigs must also consider wearing knee pads, shin guards, and bump helmet to protect them. Head injuries are prevalent amongst handlers traveling in the trailers. It is easy to get head bruises, cuts, and bumps.

Other equipment is necessary for day to day handling of the pigs include:

- Hard hats
- Shin guards
- Eye protection
- Hearing protection
- Dust mask
- Gloves
- Sort Boards
- Knee pads

Chapter 5: Pig Nutrition and Feeding

Pigs, just like most farm animals, require essential nutrients and vitamins to meet their sustenance needs. Failure to provide pigs with such nutritional requirements increases their risk of stunted growth, poor reproducing, lactation, among other functions. Good feed is a necessity for these animals. You can use locally available feeds that are affordable.

Remember that feed is the biggest cost factor in the raising of pigs and can amount to about 60% to 80% of the total cost of production. Pigs can be fed using kitchen and vegetable waste. The food must be of the right quantity and mixture. And focus on valuable sources of energy rather than achieving feed efficiency or growth rate. However, their nutritional requirements can be divided into five categories; carbohydrates, fats, proteins, minerals, and vitamins.

How do pigs digest food?

Pigs consume food with their mouth, where the digestion process begins. Pigs are omnivorous animals with one of the best feeds to meat ratio. As piglets, they are born with needle teeth. As they grow, boars grow tusks and canines, which they use as weapons if they feel threatened. Their molars have numerous tubercles, make them ideal for crushing food.

Food is chewed into smaller bits, which is then mixed with saliva, making it easy to swallow. Food then passes through the esophagus and into the stomach, where it is broken down further by other enzymes to form chyme. This chyme is later broken down in the small intestines and absorbed. It doesn't stop there as food particles make their way into the large intestine (cecum and colon) where water and remaining nutrients are absorbed into the pig's body. The colon forms the feces, which are expelled through the anus.

What can you feed your pig?

Grains

You can comfortably feed your pigs commercially prepared or locally made grains. Cereal grains are the world's leading source of energy in foods in both humans and animals. For your pigs, consider a total feed mixture constituting approximately 55% to 65% of grains. Grains are primarily energy-providing foods, but they also contribute to approximately 20-50% of all protein content in the food mixture.

For instance:

- Broken rice contains approximately 8% protein.

- Maize is also a great feed option that is high in digestible energy. It can be the primary source of energy in the feed mixture. Maize is an affordable food option in many countries, especially in South America and Africa.

- Oats are good energy sources but cannot constitute over 40% of a mixture for growing pigs and less than 60% in mature pigs.

- Sorghum has properties like maize. Consider using one as a substitute for the other.

• Wheat (feed grade) is also a great source of energy and protein that can be used in the feed mix. It is a great alternative to maize but is slightly more expensive compared to maize. Yet, using wheat could potentially save you a lot in food expenses, as you might not need to buy more protein.

• Barley is an energy source high in dietary fiber, which is excellent for digestion. Consider keeping the barley content in the feed mix less than 70%.

There are grain by-products such as maize bran, wheat bran, and maize cobs used to lower the digestible energy of the food mixture. Additionally, such brans are rich in protein and are relatively affordable. The most popular grain by-product is wheat bran. It is cost-effective and rich in protein. However, it does have a laxative effect on pigs.

Fishmeal

Fishmeal is a brown powder/flour derived from the cooking, drying, and crushing of raw fish. Fish is a well-known source of protein. Pig keepers widely use fishmeal in feed mixtures across the world.

Blood and Carcass Meal

Blood meal is a form of animal feed made from the blood of cattle or hogs as a by-product of the slaughterhouse. It is high in protein and is one of the highest non-synthetic sources of nitrogen. But its dense nutritional value does not warrant extensive use of this meal because the blood meal is unpalatable. Consider limiting blood meal to 5% in the feed mixture.

Vegetables and Fruits

You will notice that most pigs are fairly happy eating broccoli, tomatoes, oranges, kale, spinach, cabbages, melons, potatoes, beets, carrots, apples, and cucumbers. Most vegetables, fruits, and even bread scraps (that have not been tampered with) are pig treats. If they are by-products, they should be cooked properly.

Lucerne is a common plant option used in feed mixtures. It is high in fiber but low in digestible energy. As a result, consider limiting Lucerne in the feed mix. Other common plant options include soya bean oil cake meal and sunflower oil cake meal, which are high in plant protein.

Soybeans can act as a protein supplement for pigs above 25 lbs. (approximately 11 kg). Growing pigs have a limited ability to process the complex proteins usually found in soybean meals. Additionally, developing pigs may develop allergies to certain proteins found in this meal.

Sources of Minerals in Pigs

In pigs, minerals play a vital role in their development, performance, and overall well-being. Minerals are helpful in the formation and development of bones, lactation in sows, and certain chemical reactions in the body. For such reasons, pigs require about 13 different minerals. Out of the 13 minerals, the following should be routinely added to their feed mixture—calcium, zinc, iodine, manganese, phosphate, copper, sodium, iron, and selenium. Minerals for pigs are divided into two groups: trace (micro) minerals and macro minerals.

• Calcium is one of the most deficient major minerals in diets comprising of oilseed meals and grains. Additionally, calcium affects the absorption of other minerals, such as zinc. Feed lime is a great and affordable source of calcium, but it does not contain phosphate. For this mineral, consider giving the pigs bone meal.

• Sodium is essential as it helps with nerve function. The deficiency of this mineral leads to impaired growth and loss of appetite. The grains listed above are great for energy but poor in mineral supplementation. This problem can be solved by simply adding salt (sodium chloride) to the food. If the food is too salty, consider providing adequate water to reduce the toxicity. Failure to do so can cause weakness, seizures, or even death of the pigs.

- Iron is required for the synthesis of hemoglobin necessary for oxygen in the red blood cells. Piglets are born with high concentrations of iron in their livers. Lactating sows usually need iron as their milk is the only way piglets can get their nutrients and it doesn't contain iron. Consider giving these pigs iron supplementation in the form of injections or tablets administered through the feed mix. Iron deficiency in pigs leads to these symptoms; pale mucous membranes, enlarged heart, spasmodic (contraction of the trachea) breathing, reduced immunity, and lowered immunity.

- Selenium is an important mineral used in developing enzymes that protect cells against oxidative damage. In the United States, most areas lack this mineral in the soil, while few locations have it in abundance. For this reason, check the soil in which your farm or pig's husbandry is located. Deficiency signs of selenium include muscle dystrophy, sudden death, especially in growing piglets, impaired reproduction, and liver necrosis, among others.

- Zinc is a major mineral necessary for the development of normal skin and many enzymes. Deficiency symptoms include rough, cracked, or scaly skin, loss of appetite, and impaired sexual development. Zinc concentration is low in plants and grains; however, this mineral is abundantly found in animal products such as a bone meal.

- Just like zinc, copper is an essential mineral needed for the formation and function of a couple of enzymes. Also, this mineral is necessary for the absorption of iron from the intestinal tract and liver. Most crops have a sufficient supply of this mineral. Copper supplementation is necessary as it stimulates growth and feeds intake in pigs, especially weaning pigs. Copper deficiency symptoms include heart enlargement, stunted growth, nervous disorders, poor development of bones, and hemoglobin-deficient red blood cells. But exposure to high levels of copper include impaired growth, anemia, and in extreme cases, death.

• Manganese is necessary for enzyme function influencing bone development, metabolism, and reproduction. Signs and symptoms of manganese deficiency include a general imbalance in developing pigs, lactation problems in sows, enlarged hocks, and stunted growth (which includes irregular legs), among other things. Manganese does not occur naturally in grains, and thus it is advisable to supplement this mineral in the pig's diet.

What should you not feed your pig?

Most pig owners are not aware that feeding pigs certain foods might be harmful to the swine or even illegal. For instance, feeding pigs meat or meat products in Australia is illegal. Feeding pigs these food substances could potentially introduce deadly diseases to both pigs and other livestock present on the farm. The following are foods you should not feed your pigs.

Meat or Meat Products

You must not feed pigs meat or meat products. This is illegal in some countries. Additionally, the CSIRO Australian Animal Health Laboratory testing on pork products showed in 2019 that out of 418 tested samples, 202 tested positive for the African Swine Fever (ASF). Pig related studies and surveys have shown there is a direct relationship between ASF and meat or meat products. Avoid feeding meat to pigs to reduce the chances of an outbreak of the African Swine Flu. If you notice any unusual death in pigs, be quick to contact local authorities.

Food Waste and Scraps

Food waste or scraps that have potentially been in contact with meat or meat products may carry dangerous viruses, including the African Swine Flu. As a result, these viruses could provide an entry point to infect other farm animals. It is advisable to avoid such products because many viruses can survive comfortably for long periods in meat or meat products. Some say that the outbreak of foot and mouth disease back in 2011 in the UK had its roots in waste products fed to pigs. The waste food products contained meat products that carried the virus.

Refrain from feeding your pigs kitchen scraps, food from retailers including supermarkets or bakeries and rubbish dumps, meat, blood, or bones form other mammals, birds whether cooked or raw. If you don't know whether any food product has been in contact with meat or meat products, you should not feed it to pigs.

Traditional Pig Feeds

There are certain foods that pigs need to eat to meet their nutritional requirements for growth, reproduction, and overall well-being. The following are traditional foods you can give to your pigs.

• Rice Bran- Great for energy. It also contains 11% protein.

• Maize- Best source of energy, it is very cheap, and has 9% protein.

• Soy beans- Has a high nutritional value and contains 38% protein. It should be cooked with other foods such as rice bran or maize.

• Broken Rice- Another great alternative for energy. It contains about 8% protein.

• Wheat bran- Contains important dietary fiber with significant proportions of proteins, carbohydrates, minerals, and vitamins.

• Root Crops- As the name suggests, root crops are underground plant parts frequently consumed by both humans and animals. They should never be over 30% of the feed mix. They should be washed, peeled, sliced, and dried because of the toxic substances found on root plant skins.

• Fruits- Fruits can be given to pigs *fresh*. If they have been tampered with during transportation, consider boiling them before feeding the pigs. Suitable fruits include bananas, papaya, melons, and apples, just to mention a few.

• Screened restaurant or kitchen waste- Waste can be given to pigs but it needs to be screened first because of potential contamination. Either way, consider boiling or properly cooking such food items before feeding the pigs.

• Vegetables- Vegetables can be given while still fresh. If they are damaged or tampered with during transportation, they should be boiled. They are supplementary feeds for pigs, i.e., spinach, cabbage, morning glory, and lettuce, among others.

• Ipil-Ipil- These are locally available tree crops. These plants are nutritional and are rich in protein. Consider mixing them with other feeds before feeding the pigs.

• Banana Stem- Pigs enjoy eating banana stems. Consider chopping them down into small bits and adding salt before feeding the pigs.

• Cola-Cassia- This plant is rich in crude protein, calcium, iron, thiamine, phosphorus, vitamin C, niacin, and riboflavin.

• Green Soya Bean Plant

• Pumpkin- They are an excellent source of vitamins, including vitamin B. Be careful when preparing pumpkins as many vitamins are lost during the preparation process.

• Other plants you should feed your pig include water hyacinth, clovers, alfalfa, mulberry, chayote, and winter melon.

Pigs and Their Feed Requirements

Boars

When feeding boars, it is important to remember that they must not be fat or too lean. Consider feeding your boars 2 kg of feed mix daily. Keep a close eye on them; if they grow too thin, consider adding extra feed every day. If they grow too fat, consider reducing the daily feed. If the boar is regularly used for breeding, then increase the feed to about 2.5 kg daily.

Dry/Pregnant Sows and Gilts

After the weaning process, consider giving the sows a feed mixture of approximately 2 kg daily. Keep the sows in good condition during this period i.e., just like the boars, monitor the weight and fat of the pregnant sows. The weaner meal should be about 0.25 kg extra for every suckling pig.

Lactating Sows

Lactating sows (sows with piglets) require a lactation mixture, especially those with many piglets. Additionally, they should not lose weight or lose as little weight as possible. A sow in good shape should be fed more than 2 kg., with sows with over six piglets should be fed at least 6 kg of feed and lactation mixture every day. Also, they always have access to clean and fresh water.

Young Piglets (Up to 10 Weeks Old)

When feeding young piglets, it is important always to make their feed dry (creep pellets). Consider using a self-feeder so that no feed goes to waste. Remember that pigs in this stage need to eat as much as possible to stimulate quick growth. The feed should be approximately 0.25-100 kg per day after seven days up to the day they start weaning.

Growing Pigs (11 to 13 Weeks Old)

After the pigs have been weaned, they will grow at an incredible rate. Growing pigs are excellent for good quality meat with low-fat percentage. However, just like the young piglets, always consider feeding these pigs with a self-feeder.

Remember that pig appetite is important to their overall growth and development. Pigs are clean animals who eat fresh and clean meals as opposed to stale or even contaminated meals. You should clean their feed and water troughs frequently; also remember that maintaining adequate feeder space is important to allow the pigs to feed whenever they want.

Chapter 6: Pig Health, Care, and Maintenance

Pig's welfare is an important aspect that directly affects the quality of meat. The welfare of a pig includes its physical wellbeing, mental wellbeing, and natural living. These aspects can be compromised by extended periods of being confined, barren environments, or mutilation. Transporting pigs over long distances can also affect their welfare negatively.

This chapter will show you how to care for your pig properly, and the diseases they are prone to, as well as the currently available treatments. The topics help to provide the best care for your pig for quality meat.

Diseases and Welfare of Pigs

Pig Welfare

A pig's welfare is not merely an issue of health and diseases; their welfare also involves the *ethical aspect* of farming. This is especially true in terms of slaughter and transport. There are different perspectives on animal welfare, depending on cultural backgrounds. In small farms, pig production is directly influenced by welfare practices. Their productivity and health will be improved as the treatment improves.

Transport and Slaughter

Poor transportation creates stress in pigs. Pigs do not have sweat glands; hence they become very susceptible to heat, especially during transport. Many pigs die every year while being transported.

Welfare Issues of Castration

Most farmers castrate pigs without giving them pain relievers or anesthetics. This causes the pigs to suffer short-term and long-term pain. Castration also makes the pigs more susceptible to infections due to the open wound. Most farmers administer no pain relievers due to the extra time and costs involved.

The anesthetic should be administered one hour before the procedure. Make sure that the anesthetic is non-aversive. NOTE: There are some countries, such as Switzerland, that have banned castration.

Tooth Clipping

The teeth of the piglets are usually clipped immediately after being born. The purpose is to prevent injuries from occurring. This happens frequently when they are trying to locate the teat of the sow. Sows are not always able to cater to the growing litter due to their poor health, or if the litter is simply too large to handle. To increase the survival rate, tooth clipping is crucial, or the strongest pigs will overwhelm the rest.

The teats located at the front of the body have the most milk. The teats, located at the back, have progressively less milk. Once a piglet has chosen a teat, they will defend it at all costs.

House of Fattening Pigs

Pigs intended for meat production are kept in crowded and barren conditions. This is usually in slatted concrete floors with no rooting devices. The pigs cannot access the outdoors and have not experienced fresh air nor daylight. They do not behave naturally and tend to be frustrated and bored. They are usually fighting and biting each other, leading to injuries. Pigs also experience tail cutting that causes stress, infections, and conflicts.

Farrowing Crate

A sow or gilt is moved to a farrowing crate before the date of giving birth. This is often confused for a sow stall. The significant difference is space for the piglets. The bars in the crate prevent the sow from crushing the piglets. Just like sow stalls, the movement of the sow is highly restricted. The sow cannot roam freely to build a nest for the piglets, nor is she able to retreat from the piglets when they bite her teats.

Farrowing crates are allowed in most countries, but the practice is banned in Sweden, Switzerland, and Norway.

Sow Stalls

As much as it is common to put a pregnant sow in a stall for 16 weeks, this practice can be quite harmful. The stalls serve as a mental cage for the sow. They are usually bare concrete floors that are narrow, preventing the sow from even turning around. The sow can only lie down or stand up – and with a lot of difficulty.

Sow stalls prevent the sow from her natural behaviors. They cannot socialize, forage, exercise, or explore, and they prevent the sow from going outside. Pigs naturally love to explore the environs; caging them makes them frustrated and stressed.

Sow stalls increase abnormal behavior in pigs. They tend to bar-bite, indicating very high-stress levels. Many researchers have likened their behavior in a stall to clinical depression. The feed is customarily limited during pregnancy, thereby increasing the frustration levels of the sow.

The stalls are banned in UK and Sweden but are popular in the rest of the world. They are encouraged when the sow is still weaning the previous litter until the end of four weeks of pregnancy.

Diseases

The most crucial factor when starting your pig farm is to be sure the pigs you are purchasing are of good health. You must obtain the health reports of each pig to establish their condition and wellbeing. You can ask your veterinary doctor to accompany you during the purchase for assistance in understanding (and assessing) common diseases pigs are prone to; many can be fatal. Below are common pig diseases, along with their symptoms and preventative steps.

Pre-Weaning Stage Diseases

1. Exudative Dermatitis

This is also known as *greasy pig disease*. It's an infection brought on by a bacterium called Staphylococcus hyicus. Its primary symptom is skin lesions which look like black spots on the skin, spreading and becoming flaky and/or greasy. The disease can be fatal, should it be left untreated.

You can easily treat this infection with a series of antibiotics, autogenous vaccines, and skin protectants. To prevent the disease from spreading or occurring, make sure the hygienic standards of the pen are high. Consider avoiding teat dipping during the healing process. Reduce the chances of skin abrasions to prevent the infection from entering the skin system. Abrasions may occur due to sharp equipment and rough floors.

2. Coccidiosis

An incredibly prevalent parasite among suckling pigs caused by three types of coccidia. The primary symptoms are diarrhea with bloody spots in piglets over 21 days of age. Extreme conditions can be remedied with coccidiostats and fluid therapy. Due to damage to the intestines, pigs are prone to secondary infections.

The sows should be treated to prevent the spread of the disease. The feces of the sows can pose a huge risk as they carry many types (and much) bacteria. The best way to prevent this disease from occurring is to maintain a clean and dry environment for the pigs.

Post-Weaning Diseases

1. Respiratory Diseases

It is easy to identify a respiratory disease among pigs, as they will cough, sneeze, experience heavy breathing, stunted growth, and, in extreme cases, death. You must administer antibiotics either through water, food, or injectable substances. Inadequate ventilation can also increase respiratory diseases.

Some strains of pneumonia can be curtailed by administering vaccines, so it is crucial to identify the type of strain present to fight it efficiently. Overcrowding and unhygienic housing are also critical factors for respiratory infections.

2. Swine Dysentery

Pigs with this type of infection often have diarrhea with traces of blood in their feces. This infection is caused by a bacterium known as Brachyspira hyodsenteriae. Pigs that have completed weaning have a reduced growth rate or even death when infected.

The infection can easily be treated by antibiotics administered through food, water, or injectable substances. You can reduce stock density to minimize infection and you can easily improve the hygiene of the pen and control the rodents in it. The disease is prevalent when new stock is bring introduced to the pen.

Breeding Stage Diseases

1. Mastitis

A bacterial infection prevalent in sows that causes an infection in the mammary glands, resulting in skin discoloration. The significant symptoms of mastitis are reduced milk production, loss of appetite, and increased body temperature. Mastitis can be treated efficiently by anti-inflammatory drugs or antibiotics.

The best way to prevent this disease is by increasing the standards of hygiene. It is essential to maintain healthy nutrition during the late stages of pregnancy. Stress can also cause this disease, especially if the teats are harmed by the housing facilities.

2. Porcine Parvovirus

This disease mostly occurs in pregnant sows and is common in gilts, affecting reproduction immensely. If present in pig litters, they will suffer an increased decline in size due to mummification and stillbirths. This disease is fairly challenging to diagnose as its symptoms are crosscutting on other reproductive diseases. The parvovirus can exist outside the host for several weeks.

There are no treatments of this disease, hence the need to take preventive measures.

Other Diseases

1. Malnutrition

This is a common pig disease that is very easy to identify. The symptoms are stunted growth and visible thinness. Healthy pigs are not bony; the only bones visible are the shoulder blades. If the farmer can also see the backbone, ribs, or hips, then the pigs are too thin. Pigs grow rapidly over a few weeks; if they are growing slowly, then consider malnutrition as the foremost factor.

Malnutrition is caused due to poor quality feed. Piglets that have completed weaning require high quality of feed compared to adults. Lactating sows also need high-quality feed to produce milk.

2. Lice and Flies

Lice and flies infestation can cause the spread of infectious diseases. It is easy to spot the lice on pigs as they are unusually large. They lead to blood loss and bacterial infection. Flies are a threat because they can land on open wounds and result in diseases. Spraying the pigs can reduce the flies and lice. You must maintain high hygienic standards and use fly traps.

3. Parasites

Pigs are prone to many parasites including roundworms and tapeworms. Roundworms live in the gut and look like a worm. Pigs with parasites experience sudden weight loss. Young pigs are the most prone to parasitic infections. If not treated, parasites can block the entire gut, leading to death. Dewormers are efficient in flushing them out of the intestinal system.

Tapeworms usually reside in the muscles of the pigs resulting in pig measles. Pigs usually have pain and difficulty moving. It is not advisable to eat meat infested with tapeworms as it can cause human health problems. There is no cure for infected pigs, so farmers should take measures to prevent the pigs from wandering around the farm.

4. Self-Poisoning

This occurs due to improper feeding. Feeding pig's food from various restaurants may not be ideal. The pigs may experience blindness, lose balance, vomit, and experience seizures. Farmers should always check on the quality of the food they give their pigs.

5. African Swine Fever

It is caused by the Asfarviridae family of viruses, which differs from the classical swine fever; the fever can be caused from contaminated feed, lice bites, ticks, other infected pigs, and contaminated medical equipment.

There is no treatment for this disease, and it is, therefore, essential to prevent it in the first place. Infected pigs should be isolated immediately after the disease has been detected.

6. Foot and Mouth Disease

This is caused by picornaviridae aphthovirus. Its symptoms are excessive salivation, fever, loss of appetite; it can be deadly.

A farmer should routinely take his pigs for vaccination to protect the breeding stock as it is a prevalent disease during the winter. Other farm animals will only spread it.

7. Rabies

This disease is transferable to humans. Its symptoms are nerve disorders, aggression, paralysis, and often leads to death. The symptoms evolves very quickly in pigs, and they tend to become shaky, aggressive, shriek, quickly attack, and have a hoarse voice. Rabies is usually fatal and has no cure.

Tips to Prevent Diseases in Pigs

As a farmer, you must know the measures you should take to prevent diseases from infecting your breeding stock. There are some treatable diseases, but others can be very damaging to the breeding stock. When preventing diseases, consider the following approach;

• Pigs must be enclosed in spaces with good hygiene levels. The area should not be prone to overcrowding and poor ventilation.

• The farmer should constantly communicate with the vet to prevent looming diseases, identify existing ones, and cure health problems. They should be notified upon any death.

• All pigs should be purchased from registered sources. Make sure the area is clean and properly managed.

• A farmer should know of what he feeds the pigs. It is not advisable to feed the pigs with general waste from restaurants or households

• It would help if you also complied with the regulations of pig welfare. This is crucial, especially when transporting the swine.

- It is vital to collaborate with veterinarians to avoid any hiccups. This will ensure a smooth transition when examining the pigs medically.

- Make sure the fresh meat you sell or consume is examined by veterinary experts to avoid serious repercussions.

- Neutralization units or local authorities should handle the bodies of dead animals or infected pigs.

Medicines

Medication can be administered in different ways, depending on the medicine. Some can be fatal when injected and hence need to be administered orally. Other medications can be applied only topically and absorbed through the skin. The following are some of the conventional methods of administering medication:

Oral

Most antibiotics are administered through the mouth.

Topical

The medicine is applied to the skin. A farmer can use a spray to apply on the surface.

By Injection

The injection can be intradermal, intramuscular, subcutaneous, or intravenous.

Via Uterus

Antibiotics can be inserted into the anterior vagina when infected.

Via Rectum

This is not a common method of administering drugs. It is used on pigs that suffer from salt poisoning.

Use the information on the bottle to guide you on the method of administration. If you are having trouble, always consult a veterinary doctor.

Taking Care of A Pig

Pigs are intelligent animals, and if brought up clean from birth, they will not deviate. There are different stages of pigs as they grow; starter, grower, finisher, and breeding. When raising the pigs, it is cleaner to raise them on concrete as opposed to other environs. The concrete reduces exposure to parasites. Your swine need a lot of shade and protection from the rain, wind, and snow.

Being exposed to too much heat can cause the pigs suffering from heatstroke. The exposure can cause salt toxicity, especially if there is no water. You should provide clean and fresh water. Add water every thirty minutes till the pigs have drank their fill. Lack of proper hydration may cause brain issues.

The size and age of the pigs will determine the space requirement in pen. Provide the sow with a crate while farrowing to prevent it from lying on another pig. As the pigs grow, make sure they have three feet of space.

The nutrition of the pig depends on the ages. Growing pigs require different feeds to provide them with more energy. Their feeds require more high energy content.

There must be treatments of external and internal parasites. The type of housing and history affects the inoculation. The sow is treated before breeding and a fortnight before farrowing. Treat the growing pigs, especially if they are on a dirty floor. Take a fecal sample from the growing pigs to determine the proper product to deworm. Human food scraps, especially the ones that contain meat, shouldn't be fed to pigs.

Do not feel pressured to vaccinate the pigs, especially during the hot season as this can be a source of additional stress. Administer the vaccination individually to the pigs to prevent hiccups. Use the weight of the pigs to determine their overall health.

When transporting pigs, you must obtain health certificates for the swine. Be sure to have the pigs' bill of sale in your records. It is a requirement in some states to provide such documentations when slaughtering or selling. A health certificate is crucial when traveling across different states. Using pig notches and tattoos has proven an essential aspect of identifying the pigs.

Pig Care During Different Seasons

Pigs and sows experience extreme heat during the summer as they decrease feeding, grow, and produce milk. They also suffer just as much during the winter season. Cold seasons result in slow growth, reduced feed efficiency, high infection rate, loss of body fat, and high mortality rate.

When it's too cold, pigs try to keep warm by minimizing heat loss; they shiver to increase metabolic heat production and increase food intake. However, when a pig is stressed, they avoid eating. It is essential to keep them warm, especially two weeks after arrival.

You can utilize these specific mechanisms to reduce heat loss. Tackle their legs beneath their body and huddle them together. Piglets and young pigs can change their sleeping and dunging to obtain warmth from their excretes. These steps will help you to ensure your pigs are always kept warm:

- It is crucial that you can identify when pigs are cold. They tend to huddle together and tuck their feet beneath their body. The pigs will develop long rough hair and become skinny.

- Make sure the pigs are dry and that their bedding is replaced frequently.

- Reduce the ventilation in the room during the cold months. Always make sure that the doors and windows are closed.

- Insulate the walls and ceilings.

- Utilize zone heating such as headlamps, creep boxes, and heated mats.

- Avoid multiple stressors. Vaccinating, weaning, castrating, transporting, changing the environment, and changing feeds can induce chilling.

When Should You Contact A Vet?

Disease prevention is still a significant challenge among farmers, and new diseases are continually cropping up in pigs. The condition is a threat to the pigs, and the food supply on the farm. Some measures are taken to prevent diseases: food safety and adopting suitable pig farming activities. However, the most important is biosecurity. It is an important management tool to curtail the spread of disease.

Veterinarians are involved on a day-to-day basis in taking of the pigs. Their role today has evolved beyond merely treating sick pigs. They are useful when being consulted, managing, and even constructing a new farm.

Veterinarians are crucial in taking medicine inventory, considering weather and feed, taking lab samples for testing, managing disease outbreaks, and calculating withdrawal dates. The following are examples of when a pig farmer should consult a veterinarian:

- Testing for viruses and administering vaccinations

- Oversee health management plans

- Assessing sows individually

- Ensuring safe delivery of the newborn and take care of new moms

The basic needs of a modern pig are to increase production and efficiency. For maximum profitability, a veterinary doctor is key. A routine monthly checkup can save you from a lot of problems. The monthly visit should be instrumental in creating more awareness of the farm-related problems and develop procedures to solve them. A veterinary doctor increases efficiency, contributes to the management, educates the farmer, controls diseases, and prevents diseases.

A farmer must accompany the vet in his routine checkups to give observations. It is vital that during this time, the farmer discusses with the vet the weaknesses and strengths of the breed. Obtain a written report for evidence. It will serve as a reminder of the discussions and a highlight of the recommendations.

Chapter 7: Pig Reproduction and Breeding

Reproduction is an important factor with profitability in the pig industry. This is because the number of pigs, sows, and weaning pigs every year is crucial for the profits of many investors in the pig industry. This number is heavily reliant on the total number of pigs per litter reproduced by a sow. The reproduction of weaning piglets depends on the breeding of these animals. The piglets must be able to grow fast in a short period while producing quality carcasses, with low fat and plenty of meat.

It is essential you buy breeding animals of high quality. The pigs should come from a farm with high standards of nutrition, hygiene, and overall management. If it is your first time, consider having a professional or experienced individual to help you make the right choice. This topic will help you further understand pig breeding and reproduction.

A breed can be defined as a group of animals who share the same ancestry with identifiable traits. When this group of animals mate, they produce offspring with the same qualities. The main purpose behind breeding is to achieve desired traits deemed as profitable.

Pig Mating or Breeding Systems

As mentioned above, breeding pigs requires significant knowledge or experience handling such practices. When buying breeding pigs, consider ones that have been well fed and kept in sanitary conditions. If you are running a small-scale farm, then consider the following selection criteria when selecting boars, gilts, and sows:

• Consider buying above average purebred boars. Pure breeding involves breeding pigs of the same breed. The main purpose of pure breeding is the identification and propulsion of "superior" genes to be used in the commercial production of meat.

• When buying boars, consider buying prominent breeds used in your country.

• When buying gilts or young female pigs, it is crucial to purchase them from a reputable vendor who keeps records of the pigs. Gilts can be used as purebreds or cross-bred pigs. Also, consider buying gilts from the same vendor. It is important to seek expert opinion on such matters to help you identify the appropriate breeding policy.

• Should you choose to select your own gilts, apply strict measures and keep accurate growth and feed conversion records.

• Your selection of a gilt should be based on the size of the litter, i.e., consider choosing a gilt with 12 teats to serve a large litter.

• Consider choosing gilts at least eight months old and approximately 120 kgs (264 lbs.) before their first service.

• Gilts chosen from sows that wean approximately eight to ten piglets for every litter are linked with good motherhood. The sows should have their first farrowing after a year and the second farrowing seven months from the first.

• The choice of gilt or boars should be based on their ability to grow fast. In the foreseeable future, this will prove less costly to keep, as they consume less as they gain healthy weight with reasonable body fat.

- Consider choosing gilts with proper teats; i.e., not inverted or having fat deposits at the base of the teats

- It would be best if you chose gilts with well-developed hams. Before you start the mating process, consider exposing the gilts to the heat of about two to three days. However, for gilts, they should mate after the first day of their heat period while sows should mate on their second day of the same.

- Boars should be well developed, with sound feed, proper hams, and a good overall length. Additionally, these developments should extend to the teats; they should have 12 primary teats to increase the chances of passing on this desirable trait.

- Consider the biggest boar from the litter to use as a sire. If castration is to be done, it needs to be four weeks after the breeding process has been completed.

- Just like the gilt's age considerations, the boar should also be at least eight months old before their first service.

Breeding and mating systems are methods used for pairing boars and sows (and sometimes gilts) to achieve profitable and desired traits in the offspring. Genetics play a massive role in the overall productivity and performance of the pigs. Pig farmers are urged to be familiar with such methods.

It involves two primary strategies; positive assertive mating and negative assertive mating. With positive assertion in mating, breeding occurs to increase the chances of achieving desired traits while reducing the odds of undesirable odds. Negative assortative mating involves breeding two different pigs to rectify the expression of a certain trait. The following are common breeding systems that pig keepers.

Outbreeding

Outbreeding involves mating pigs of the same breed but with slight relations to the average breed. It is also known as outcrossing. Simply put, there shouldn't be a common ancestor among the mating pigs for a couple of generations.

Inbreeding

This breeding system involves linking two closely related pigs within the same breed. The relationship could be anything from mother and son, daughter and father, or siblings with siblings. As a result, one can concentrate common and desirable genes in the offspring. However, expect a reduction in the litter size. The following are other effects of inbreeding

Effects of Inbreeding

- Inbreeding increases mortality rates in pigs. You will notice certain limitations in the overall physical function with instabilities. Additionally, when the sow cannot move, the risk of mortality is significantly increased.

- Inbred boars tend to have low sex drive.

- Separation of the offspring or parents severely affects the pigs. The main purpose behind breeding is to create desirable traits in pigs for commercial purposes. Once the male or female piglets are taken away, the stress might affect the remaining pigs or piglets negatively.

- Breeding between siblings might not always bring out the desired outcome.

- Approximately 25% to 50% of the piglets are usually born smaller and weaker compared with the first sow. Additionally, some of the piglets are born dead.

- The overall number of piglets in a litter is significantly smaller.

Cross-Breeding

Cross-breeding involves a careful and planned approach to mating pigs. It entails mating two pigs with different backgrounds. This results in heterosis, which is the improved productivity and performance of offspring, especially when compared to the previous generation. Heterosis occurs when different breeds of pigs are mated with each other as a correction mechanism of traits exhibited in the earlier generations.

Cross Breeding Strategies

- **Terminal System**

This system of breeding is one of the most common systems used across the United States. Pig farmers running large scale commercial operations frequently use a terminal cross-breeding stem. The terminal system involves a terminal that provides the desired genetic traits to maximize pig growth, development, feed efficiency, and the quality of the carcass. The terminal sire could either be a purebred or a cross-bred. Terminal systems result in developing "superior" pigs that should meet the demands of your audience or target market. This simple system has created genetically uniform groups of hogs annually in the United States. Also, this system brings out hybrid vigor in all the females and their offspring.

Hybrid vigor is the tendency of offspring to exhibit superior genetic traits, especially when compared to the previous generation. One major downside associated with terminal systems is the perennial purchase of boars and gilts. You will be forced to replace all the gilts and boars after selling them to your target market. This process may be costly. Additionally, some pigs may introduce pathogens, causing diseases to the remaining herd of animals.

- **Rotational Systems**

If you consider your farm operations small scale, then consider using a rotational system. Just like terminal systems, rotational systems are also simple and efficient. It is also known as the back-crossing system or the two-breed rotational system, which includes only two breeds. This system is cheap and affordable for most small-scale pig keepers. Unlike the terminal sire systems, rotational systems do not maximize hybrid vigor. But with technology and the purchase of semen, some of these barriers in rotational systems have been significantly reduced.

- **Combination System**

As the name suggests, this strategy of cross-breeding combines the functionality of the two methods mentioned above. For instance, a small group of the herd is kept in the rotational system to produce female pigs for the entire farm. Afterward, the gilts are serviced with terminal sires to ensure that most (if not all) of the offspring's genetic traits are easily sellable in the market. For a small-scale farmer, this system can be hectic because of the insufficient labor. And this method requires meticulous management and record-keeping for success.

Breeding systems influence the genetic make-up of your pigs; such methods play a vital role in the carcass quality and overall performance of your pig. Because of the perks of heterosis, cross-breeding countries like the United States have become popular. For small scale pig keepers, rotational systems are the most affordable and practical system to use, especially when using artificial insemination.

Effects of Cross Breeding

- Leads to piglets with local sows.

- Brings about piglets with exotic sows.

- The local sow can bear bigger and healthier piglets.

- Piglets borne from cross-breeding are strong, healthy, and grow fast.

- From a financial standpoint, cross-breeding is profitable as most piglets are sold, and a few are selected for cross-breeding.

• The stronger and healthier pigs are sold or castrated for meat purposes leaving behind weak piglets that cannot be used for further cross-breeding

• Negative breed selection results in smaller and weaker piglets, 50% of which will die during or after birth.

• Negative selection results in a small litter size.

Line Breeding

Passing undesirable traits results from negative selection inbreeding. The closer the relationship of the parents, the higher the risk of passing on undesirable traits in the next generation. The traits are *phenotypic*, meaning that results will affect the pig's health, productivity, and overall wellbeing. This breeding method is like breeding, but it focuses on a particular characteristic.

This is not easily achievable as the genetic pool can be limiting. Fortunately, technology has helped pig keepers identify the relationship between pigs. Furthermore, you can use artificial insemination to help you reduce the risk of using related boars in the breeding process. One mistake that breeders make is using multiple boars from the same litter for the siring process. Consider a maximum of one boar from each litter; otherwise, you might be reducing genetic diversity not only in your farm but also your country.

Random Mating Within a Breed

Random mating involves selecting pigs with no considerations, i.e., relations, genetic make-up, etc.

Mating Types

- **Pen Bred**

Pen mating is one of the three mating types that pig keepers commonly use. This process involves putting boars and sows or gilts in the same pen for a specific period of time, usually 20 to 40 days, without close supervision. This method is usually cost-effective as pig keepers get to save on labor. However, it will affect the farrowing rate.

- **Hand Mated**

This method of pig mating is used by small to medium-sized pig operation farms. Hand mating is the placement of a female in heat with a boar in the same pen, with the close supervision of a stock person. This stock person will assist the boar's penis as it enters the sows or gilts vagina. Using hand mating is effective in increasing the performance of the sows and boars.

- **Artificial Insemination**

Artificial insemination of swine is a common practice across the world. In Europe alone, most pigs have been bred by artificial insemination over the past few decades. Artificial Insemination is very helpful as it reduces the risk of diseases and weak genes by introducing desirable and "superior" genes.

Common Signs of Heat/ Estrus in Pigs

Heat, also known as estrus, is the physical manifestation of a biological need to mate because of increased hormones in pigs. Heat detection is the process of observing and identifying the pigs receptive to mating. A mature female pig that is not lactating or pregnant should cycle after three weeks. As a result, the heat cycle should last approximately 3 weeks. Signs of heat include:

- General unease or restlessness.

- White, slimy, and sticky mucus discharge.

• A general desire to mount or be mounted on by other pigs; can be spotted mounting other pen mates.

• Twitching ears.

• Rigid (legs and back), also known as being *locked up.*

• In females, the vulva becomes swollen and red in color.

• The female will not sit still but she will stand still if pressure is applied to her back. If someone applies pressure on her back by simply pushing down or sitting on her, the sow will stand still.

• Pigs may frequently squeal or make their voices heard.

Inducing Heat in Pigs

Stimulating the Boar, Sow, and Gilt

Boars are usually stimulated in preparation for artificial insemination. Remember that boar stimulation requires physical contact, including the occasional sniff or nudge, to arouse the female pig. Caution should be applied; consider using fence line contact.

After farrowing for the first time, a sow may take time to come into heat. Consider these techniques used by stock persons to induce heat;

• Gently stroke the sow's vagina/vulva using a freshly cut papaya stalk in the morning. Do this for three to five days.

• Bring the sow next to the boar's pen. Also, bring them before they feed. Consider bringing the sow to the boar every day for a short while just before the heat period is expected.

• You should not mate these animals during the heat of the day. Pick a time best for the boar to serve twice within 24 hours, ensuring an interval of about 12 to 14 hours between each service.

• Spray the guilt's or sow's pen with urine belonging to the boar. Do this every morning for approximately three to five days.

- To avoid boar fights and injuries, keep them in different pens/housing facilities. Consider taking the sow to the male for mating.

- Before service, have the sows/gilt consume an extra one or two kilos (approx. four pounds) of extra feed daily. After service, prolong the extra feed for another week.

- If the sow or gilt does not conceive, she will come into heat in about 21 days' time.

- If the sow or gilt manages to conceive, consider giving it an extra 0.5 kg (lbs.) extra feed mix every day. A week before farrowing gradually reduce this amount, substituting with plenty of water to prevent the congestion of the sow's/gilt's gut.

- If the sow had her first farrowing, remove all her piglets early when they grow six weeks old. All the piglets must be removed at once. Take the sow to a pen/ housing facility hosting dry sows.

- Put the sow in a location close to the boar in such a way to enable them to make contact i.e., they can smell and see each other.

How to Provide Assistance with the Mating Process

Occasionally, young boars may need assistance, as they might struggle with lining up the sow. Before you start, make sure you clean your hands and wrists. It will also help if your fingernails are short and clean.

The mating process is a slow one. The boar should take about a minute and a half before reaching the ejaculation point. To improve the conception of the sow/gilt, consider crushing one kilogram of semen nelumbinis, also known as the *lotus seed*, into the pig's feed mixture. Give this feed to the pig twice a day for about three to five days.

Culling

Culling is a term used to describe low productivity and fertility in pigs because of age or certain problems such as diseases or physical injury. Consider selling the sows that are difficult to impregnate. Also, if such sows have small litters, they should be sold off. Consider replacing them with replacement gilts or nulliparous sows (females that have never given birth, or have given birth to stillborn piglets). On the other hand, boars that are infertile should be culled, including those that are slightly fertile.

Reasons for Not Conceiving

1. Infertility

In the United Kingdom alone, infertility is the leading cause of high costs of pig production. In the United States, conception rates are above 92%, with 90% farrowing rates. Anything below these standards is considered a fertility or performance problem. There are a couple of things that lead to infertility in pigs as explained below.

• Poor Heat Detection

Heat detection is an overlooked process of pig reproduction. Most pig keepers who fail to record their first and second heat cycles risk missing out on the third cycle when sows are at their best productive cycle.

It is important to observe and record the pig's heat cycles. It is advisable to watch the pig for approximately 18 to 25 days for the first, second, and third heat cycles for the same intervals when the sow/gilt is ready to be served. It is not advisable to introduce the sow/gilt to the boar or inseminate artificially before the pig is accurately identified as standing estrus—the period in which the pig demonstrates sexual receptiveness.

Consider mating the two pigs later in the third heat cycle when the pig stands firm without moving forward. Fertility levels are high when the sow is served six days after weaning. Sows will show signs of heat before three days, but servicing them only leads to undesirable results.

- Bacterial/ Parasitic/ Viral Agents

Numerous agents could potentially cause infertility in sows and gilts. For instance, mycotoxins are caused by molds and fungi normally found in feed mixtures, including grains. Normally, all pigs are susceptible to these toxins, but in breeding pigs, it is detrimental as it causes damage to the reproduction system, causing abortion and stillbirth. Other agents include brucellosis, eperythrozoonosis, bacteria in semen, erysipelas, porcine reproductive, and respiratory syndrome (PRRS), among many others. Consider a good vaccination protocol to prevent such infectious agents from rendering your sows and gilts infertile. Also. a high-quality and stable environment will prevent seasonal infertility.

- Nutritional Deficiency

As mentioned earlier, nutrition plays a massive role in a pig's performance and ability to reproduce. Deficiency of certain minerals, vitamins, proteins, and fats can affect the pigs' ability to conceive.

- Poor Management

Management plays a crucial role in the fertility and overall performance of the pig. From weaning to mating, the entire process of growth and reproduction should be planned and properly supervised. Evaluation of reproductive soundness should be carried out when the pig is fairly young (two-and-a-half weeks old). There are other criteria you can use when evaluating the pigs for reproductive soundness, as explained in the following sub-topic.

- Unfavorable Temperatures

Recent studies have shown that temperature extremes are linked to low fertility in sows and reduced desire in boars.

2. The Sow is Overweight

If the sow is too fat or overweight, its ability to conceive is compromised.

3. The Boar is Too Young

There are optimal ages for breeding pigs, as explained above. Mating pigs at a young age, i.e. when they are below five to six months old, could lead to the inability to conceive. It is advisable to avoid premature mating in a bid to optimize reproduction as much as possible.

4. The Boar Has Been Over-Used

Over-mating a boar affects its ability to make a sow pregnant. Overworking a boar could mean mating it over five times in a week.

Factors Affecting Pigs Productivity

Genetics

A pig's genetics can have a major influence on the productivity of the pig and, eventually, the profitability of the business. The combination of nutrition, environment, and management will eventually have a major influence on productivity, size, and carcass quality.

The most common breeds of pigs include the largely white, landrace, and duroc. When selecting a boar, consider choosing such prominent breeds used worldwide, but preferably in your parent country. But commercial producers use a mix of these main breeds to take full advantage of the positive effects of cross-breeding. There are genetic improvement programs that will take account of various performance traits, including feed to meat ratio, carcass quality, and milking abilities, among others.

Nutrition

Nutritional requirements must be met for your pig to perform at an optimum level. Different pigs have different nutritional requirements, as explained in the previous chapters. For instance, boars require a different diet to lactating sows for their performance and overall output. Additionally, the quantity of the feed will influence the pig's fat levels. For optimum productivity, pig nutrition must not be overlooked.

Disease

Closely related to nutrition are diseases. Health and nutrition are two of the most critical factors affecting both the physical and economic performance of the pigs from the weaning stage until their slaughter. It is easy to argue out that good nutrition can act as a prevention for most diseases. Additionally, a good diet goes a long way in maintaining a healthy weight for pigs regardless of the stage of development.

Diseases are associated with weight loss, depending on the severity. Diseases affect the productivity of pigs in these ways;

• Certain diseases have been linked to a decrease in the insulin-like growth factor, which plays an integral function in the growth and development of pigs.

• Cytokines are a large group of proteins usually secreted as part of the pig's immune response to diseases. Cytokines are associated with the suppression of certain growth hormones. This is detrimental to the pig's growth rates and overall body size.

• Certain diseases or anorexia due to specific pathogens that compromise the pig's immunity. As a result, diseases may affect the pig's ability to eat and convert feed to meat.

• When the body is fighting pathogens, causing infections and diseases, it redirects nutrients away from tissue growth to support the body in its fight against the disease.

Environment

The environment is an important factor to consider when assessing possible outcomes to meet the intended goals regarding meat production in pigs. Too much heat will stress the pigs causing them to roll in mud as they try to cool off. And if the environment is noisy, the pigs will be continuously stressed, affecting their ability to eat and, ultimately, convert feed to meat.

Individual housing of these social animals could be very stressful to them and could ultimately compromise their welfare and productivity. It is essential to consider environmental enrichment. Remember that pigs are sensitive and intelligent animals that require special care for optimum productivity. Consider using absorbent bedding materials that create a clean, comfortable, and most important, dry environment.

Certain factors in the environment could potentially affect the pig's sense of exploration and appetite. For instance, hanging bottles, playful balls, and other things need to be changed after a while to keep the pigs interested. It is important to note that a pig's metabolism is affected by behavioral activities.

Management

When raising pigs, it is essential to note it is possible to increase their growth while reducing mortality through improving facilities and specific management practices.

Care and Management of Boar

A high degree of care and priority should be given to boars introduced to the breeding herd. The management of such animals is influential to the overall reproduction efficiency. Remember that good care and management yield reproduction and high meat quality.

• The boars should be well fed. After testing and examination of these animals has been done, the next step will be to feed them adequately. A good diet will provide the boar with sufficient energy for the mating process. Additionally, good feed will prevent the boar from becoming excessively fat. Feeding the boar goes a long way in assuring the animal remains sexually active without physical implications.

- After testing them, it is important to be cognizant of the fact that these animals' main purpose is reproduction. As a result, they should be managed and treated accordingly. It is crucial to conjure physically hardening processes for the pig, besides sexually stimulating procedures. Consider changing the boar's location, providing ample female contact through the fence line method, especially when the boars show aggressive behavior towards the females.

- The boar should be at least seven to eight months before they can be considered for breeding. The evaluation should be done before this age to make it easy to cull problematic boars.

- Observe the pig's libido. The desire to mate is crucial to breeding. Observe its aggression when mating because some may need assistance at least once in their mating life. The same goes for mounting as some may be physically injured or diagnosed with arthritis, preventing them from the successful mounting.

Chapter 8: Farrowing and Piglet Care

Good management and care can influence the health of the piglets born and their numbers. It will also affect their production levels later in life. Most deaths occur due to starvation and pre-weaning. This is common in the first few days of the piglet's life.

An excellent caretaker must know newborn piglets and their characteristics. This makes pigs overly reliant on proper care and management. Piglets are born without antibodies, and their bodies have a fat content that can last them only one day. Piglets can regulate their body temperature for only a few days. They must be taken care of and guarded against diseases that can compromise their health.

The Farrowing Process

It is necessary to know the anatomy of the pelvis and the reproductive tract for easing the farrowing process. When farrowing begins, the vulva enlarges and the vagina, leading to the opening of the womb. Lubricate your arms before inserting it into the vagina to avoid causing damage. The neck of the cervix leads to two long horns that contain the piglets.

The umbilical cord of the piglet ends at the placenta that is attached to the surface of the uterus. The cord carries the nutritional value that supplements the piglets. The placenta encloses the piglet in a sac that carries its fluids and waste products. The placenta and the sac are known as the afterbirth.

The Beginning of Farrowing

Once the piglet reaches the final stage of maturity after 115 days, farrowing begins. The pituitary and adrenal glands are activated by the piglet to produce corticosteroids. The hormones are carried via the bloodstream to the placenta. The placenta is stimulated to produce prostaglandins transported to the ovary. They are responsible for terminating the pregnancy; thus, the hormones initiate farrowing.

Length of Farrowing

The minimum period of farrowing is 115 days. Gilts have a shorter time span compared to the sows. The duration is affected by the environment, litter size, breed, and time of year.

The Farrowing Preparation

The process occurs in three stages:

Stage 1: Pre-Farrowing Period

Preparing for farrowing should start fourteen days before the day of giving birth. The teats start to enlarge, veins in the underside stand out, and the vulva swells. Farrowing reduces the appetite of the sow, and they become restless. Twelve hours to farrowing, the mammary glands of the sow can be stimulated to secrete milk. This is the best sign of farrowing. You may also spot a small mucous discharge on the vulva and around pellets of feces present. The pellets indicate that the piglet is secreting. An examination must be conducted.

Stage 2: The Farrowing Process

The process can last up to eight hours with a variation of 20 minutes between; you must check on the sow and litter in case of any harm. The gap between the first and the second sow can run up to 45 minutes. Most pigs are born headfirst, but some come out in reverse. You will notice the twitching of the tail of the pig when it is ready to give birth.

Stage 3: Delivery of the Placenta

This can last up to four hours as an indication of the farrowing process is complete. The sow will appear to be at peace, and the shivering and movement of the hind legs stop. There is usually a heavy discharge after birth for five days. At times, bacteria enter the uterus leading to inflammation commonly known as endometritis.

Farrowing Problems You Are Likely To Encounter

Step 1

The sow will be having difficulty if one these problems present itself. You will notice the lack of piglets, slow panting, and distress or blood in the vulva region. Failure to deliver the piglets can lead to these conditions:

- Rotation of the womb
- Illness of the sow
- The inertia of the womb
- Mummified pigs
- Dead pigs in the womb
- The nervousness of the sow
- Over-fat sow

Step 2

It helps to internally examined the sow using warm water and a mild antiseptic. Avoid using detergents as they can irritate the sow. Make sure your hands are washed properly, and your fingernails are short. Examine the sow as they are lying down on their side.

Problems You Might Encounter During Farrowing

Uterine Inertia

This is whereby the womb stops contracting, and two or three piglets are just beyond the cervix. If the piglets are in anterior position with legs overhead, then you can easily pull them out. In a breach pregnancy, the piglets can be delivered by raising the hind legs and clamping the hands around using the first and second fingers.

Difficult Presentations

There are certain occasions when a large piglet is daunting to birth. You can use a piece of cord and loop the center around the third finger. Use plenty of lubricants to pass the cord into the vagina. The cord is placed between the right and left ear, then secured at the jaw. Traction can help to secure the piglet.

Rotation of the Horns of the Womb

This occurs when large litters are present. The crossover between the horns distorts the cervix. Passing the hand through the cervix, you will feel the pig by reaching downwards. You must use full arms to remove the piglets.

Stimulating a Piglet to Breathe

If a piglet is delivered and it doesn't breathe, take a straw and gently poke it up its nose. This will make the piglet to cough and remove the mucus blocking the windpipe. Place your third finger across its mouth with its tongue pulled out. Place your hand around the head and swing the pig downward to remove mucus from the throat.

Step Three

If you examine the sow and detect uterine inertia, you can inject oxytocin to help it contract. This can be avoided as the arm in the vagina will stimulate more contractions. Grown pigs are capable of this venture. However, small pigs may prove difficult and result in stillbirth. You can place a piglet on the teat of the sow to help stimulate contractions.

Step Four

Once you have completed the examination and farrowing, administer antibiotics to each piglet. Penicillin is adequate to prevent any form of infection. If death occurs among the piglets, it is crucial to put antibiotics in the cervix of the sow.

Step Five

Monitor the sow for 24 hours to detect any signs of infection.

How to Care for Piglets After Birth

Caring for newborn pigs will require a good environment, adequate nutrition, and safety from diseases and crushing. Individual attention from the handler to the pigs reduces the mortality rate significantly. Labor directly affects the time you spend in the farrowing house.

Different Categories of Piglets

There are two categories that piglets are born into, normal and disadvantaged. A caretaker must know how to identify each to provide proper care. Normal piglets are born quickly and can manage a few steps. They suckle after fifteen minutes of birth. If the sow is in good condition and the farrowing environment is great, then the piglets will thrive.

Disadvantaged piglets are lightweight, foster congenital defects, are colder, and are slow to locate a teat. The longer a sow takes to farrow, the worse the condition of the piglets. They tend to be oxygen-deprived and have experienced physical trauma. The weak state of the piglets makes them unable to compete with other piglets. Chilled piglets have an low temperature that increases the mortality rate.

These techniques will help you care for your piglets.

Attended Farrowing

According to research, proper farrowing can increase the survival rate of the piglets and the number of piglets being weaned. Being present at the farrowing stage is vital to identify piglets that may need more attention.

Prevent Chilling

Farrowing quarters must reflect two climates. The sow needs a cool temperature of 65 F, and the piglets require 80 F. You can maintain the room at room temperature and provide heating for the piglets.

Makes sure you monitor the litter's responses to set the specific temperature for their thermal requirements. You will see the piglets move away from the heating zone if the temperature is too high. The temperature of the zone should be set 24 hours before farrowing. You can use heat pads, radiant heat, and headlamps to provide the necessary heat. Be careful not to place the headlamp at the rear of the sow during farrowing to reduce mortality.

Colostrum Intake

The initial milk from the teats is known as colostrum. The milk is rich in antibodies that help the piglet's fight infections. The piglets must ingest this milk for their general wellbeing. Here is a tactic to be sure the piglets get enough colostrum:

> • Regulate the temperature, so the piglets stay warm and active.

> • Split suckles to ensure all the piglets get enough time to feed. You can separate the strong ones from the teats for one or two hours. This is a great technique to be sure there is a high colostrum intake of the piglets.

Cross Fostering

This is a great strategy to reduce pig mortality by reducing litter-weight variation. It is also a great way of determining the number of functional teats. A good cross-fostering will help determine that the health status of the piglets is high and increases milk supply. Tips for effective cross-fostering:

- Be sure the piglets obtain the colostrum from their dams. This should be a minimum of six hours after birth.

- It is essential to cross foster the piglets 48 hours after they are born. Piglets identify the pig they will suckle and stick to them until weaning. This is crucial to reduce competition and to fight at the udder. When teat fidelity is not established, the piglet suffers from weight loss.

Processing Piglets

Processing piglets start from teeth clipping, clipping and treating the umbilical cord, tail docking, iron administration, treating splay-legged piglets, castration, and providing supplemental nutrients. These processes can either be performed by a specialist or a caretaker, depending on the preference. It is recommended these activities take place four days after birth to reduce the stress levels of the newborns.

Equipment

Arrange all your equipment on a trailer on wheels. The supplies and equipment must be disinfected. Gather the side cutters, supplemental iron, syringes, needles, and plastic clips on the tray.

Disease Transfer

Minimize the chances of infection while transferring piglets. Process the sick litter last, clean and disinfect the box or carts after transferring the piglets.

Persona Safety

Sows are extraterritorial after giving birth to the piglets. The sow may bite you while protecting the litter so make sure there is a partition between you and the sow.

Holding the Piglet

When trying to clip teeth, tail, and umbilical cord, hold the pig firmly. Beware of not chocking the piglet while trying to perform these processes. You can support the piglet's weight by placing your fingers under the jaw. If this is too hard on you, place the piglet on your knee carefully.

Umbilical Cord Care

The umbilical cord can foster bacteria and viruses if not taken care of properly. The cord is important to help the fetus obtain nutrients and expel waste during pregnancy. It is possible the bacteria can lead to excessive bleeding from piglets.

If there is excessive bleeding from the cord, tie it off with a string or a clamp. New-born piglets do not require their cord clamped or tied. However, if the cord is short, it can cause excessive blood loss and, eventually, death.

Needle Teeth Clipping

A newborn piglet has eight needle teeth, commonly known as wolf teeth. They are located on the sides of the upper and lower jaw. Most caretakers prefer clipping the teeth within 24 hours after birth to reduce laceration among each other. It is crucial to perform this if there is greasy pig disease or when sows are not milking well. Here are tips to assist you.

- Use cutters without blades when clipping. Do not use regular wire cutters and replace side cutters.

- Cut out one-half of the tooth. Avoid removing the whole tooth and do not crush or break it. This will prevent the piglet from nursing properly.

- Cut the tooth flat and not in an angle. The chances of the piglet causing trouble with the teeth flat are less.

Tail Docking

Tail docking is crucial to reduce cannibalism and tail biting. The process must be performed 48 hours after farrowing. This is because it can be stressful on the piglet. This age is crucial so the litter does not nibble the newly docked tail and farrowing quarters are clean. Dock the tail about an inch from the tail joint. If cut too short, the muscle activity around the anus is primarily affected. Use sterilized cutters to perform this procedure. Avoid extremely sharp objects such as a scalpel as it may lead to excessive bleeding.

Supplemental Iron

Anemia in piglets must be prevented. Iron deficiency develops rapidly in nursing pigs as there is not enough to sustain them in colostrum. There are low reserves in the newborn piglet, minimal interaction with the soil, and rapid growth.

Iron can be administered by injection or orally. The injection is a more efficient way of administering iron as it is absorbed faster, reducing the deficit. Oral iron may cause enteric disease, as it is necessary for the growth of microorganisms in the digestive tract. You can give the piglets iron when they are three days old. Try not to overdose; 200 mg is enough for them.

Creep Feeding

In addition to milk from the sows, pigs require a *creep* (supplemental food) offered to maximize weight gain during weaning. You should issue creep feed the first week away from the sow. The ration should be high-quality and ready to eat. The creep rations can be mixed at the farm or purchased. Use high energy feed that meets the nutrients of the pig.

Castration

This is the surgical removal of the two testicles and is considered routine practice for piglets meant to be slaughtered. Boars or un-castrated piglets tend to produce a bad odor during slaughtering if not removed. The best time for castration is when the piglet is two weeks old. It is easier to castrate piglets as they are easier to hold and bleed less. It is not recommended to castrate earlier because it may lead to scrotal hernias.

Examine each piglet carefully before castrating them. The scrotal hernia will make a loop of an intestine in the scrotum. Hold the piglet upright allowing the scrotum to fall, then squeeze the hind legs together. If you spot enlargement in one of the scrota, the piglet has a hernia. Avoid castrating the piglet unless you are professional and can treat the hernia properly. Most hernias are genetic.

Post-Castration Care

You must regularly check on the castrated animals for bleeding or infected tissue. Try applying pressure on the wound for two minutes to prevent further bleeding. You can consult a professional to confirm that the wound is healing well.

Record Keeping

It is highly recommended that caretakers use records to establish the strengths and weaknesses of the pigs. Reproductive traits are heritable to the piglets, and it is crucial to take that into account. It is a great way to establish superior sows. This improves the lactation performance of the sows. Consider the birth date and cause of death, pedigree information, number of piglets weaned, and the weaning weight. Record remarks of any unusual characteristic of the piglets.

Prevention of Spread of Diseases Among Piglets

Ensure that the piglets are safe and healthy. Consider the source and handling of primary and replacement breeding stock, rules governing the movement of people, the layout of the farm, and the location of the new farm and cleaning the farrow quarters. The most critical period in the pig's life cycle is the time between birth and weaning. Two pigs per litter are lost during this dire period. Poor management is the leading cause of death. The piglets can die due to crushing, bleeding from the navel, starvation, anemia, and disease.

Chapter 9: Homestead Butchering and Processing

Disclaimer: The chapters above have promoted the raising of pigs in an ethical and animal-friendly way. The following chapter contains graphic details about the butchering, slaughtering, and processing of pigs. Needless to say, the topic might not be for everyone. Some may find the information disturbing and alarming. If you plan on raising pigs for pets and nothing more, then you might consider skipping this chapter.

The crisis that brought the world to its knees in 2020 caused major disruptions to supply chains across the world. Nearly all commodities in the market, including items in the pig industry, have seen their supply and distributions chains suffer. Many people keeping pigs have been forced to seek alternative options to market or distribute their products, and customers have also been forced to look for alternative options for sourcing their meat.

One option that seeks to reduce production costs involves butchering at home. Pig keepers with a ready market can sell pigs (alive or dead) directly to consumers. The following is intended to help you understand the proper techniques used in slaughtering pigs at home. As inhumane as butchering sounds, there are procedures that, when followed, result in a humane slaughter followed by the safe production of meat. If not done appropriately, it can increase personal safety risks, animal welfare, and meat safety.

Skills and Necessary Equipment Needed for Butchering a Pig

Before butchering a pig at home, there are several skills and equipment you should have.

- Knowledge of how to handle a firearm. Slaughtering a pig starts with taking away its life. Most people prefer using a 22-caliber rifle to do this. Whatever the case, you must know how to use a firearm.

- Your ability to handle knives should be impeccable. It doesn't stop there; there are other sharp tools such as saws you should fully know. Knowledge of handling knives will help you slaughter the pig quickly and effectively. For instance, did you know that a blunt knife is more dangerous than a sharpened one? Dull knives require added pressure when cutting. This increases the risk of injury to both you and your loved ones.

- You should know how to deal with animals in a humane way. It is imperative you learn how to restrain the pig safely. It would be best if you learned how to restrict the pig's movement because failure to do so makes it much harder to stun the hog in a humane way.

- It would be best if you learned the correct procedures before starting. There is a certain degree of patience and attention to detail you need to observe to ensure that both the animal and carcass are handled in the right way.

Skills and knowledge of handling animals and relevant equipment are an absolute must when it comes to handling pigs. Once you have built these skills, then the next step is to evaluate your equipment inventory.

- Firearms and Stunning Equipment

Electrically stunning the pig with a captive-bolt stunner renders it immediately unconscious. Once the pig is no longer conscious, shooting it with a 22-caliber rifle is the most humane way to kill it.

- Knives

It is advisable to have a couple of sharp knives. From skinning knives to bone saws, consider having a few knives measuring at least six inches.

- Constant supply of water

You should consider having a metal barrel to heat the water. If a metal barrel is out of the question, consider a different heating source capable of heating water to about 150° F (65° C). Slaughtering pigs requires a decent amount of water.

- Chains and Ropes

These are used in transporting the animal after it has been killed. (While alive, at no point should the animal be restrained using chains or ropes, and restraining should never be done manually.)

- Tractor

It is effective to lift the animal into the air to process it further. A tractor will help you accomplish such a task. If a tractor is not an option, then consider a pulley system.

- Containers for waste and other inedible materials
- Consider having an experienced friend to guide you during the entire process
- Cleaning supplies
- Refrigerator

Have a storage system to help you preserve the freshness of the meat; a refrigerator will work. If that is not an option, then consider having a storage mechanism capable of getting below 40° F (4° C) as swiftly as possible.

Once you have all the tools and skills mentioned above, the next step is to slaughter the hog. Consider withholding feed from the animal for approximately 12 to 24 hours. Doing this reduces the risk of contaminating the carcass with fecal matter, and it makes it easier to gut the animal. That said, make sure the animal has had a constant supply of fresh water for drinking.

Steps for Pig Slaughter

Weather Considerations

If you live in a humid or hot area, consider starting the process early in the morning to avoid the unfavorable heat of the day. Also, consider the dust, wind, and debris that could contaminate the meat should you butcher the animal outside.

Preparing the Animal for Slaughter

At the time of slaughter, the pig should be normal, psychologically and physically. Furthermore, the animal should be well-rested. Consider resting them the night before, especially if they have been moved from one location to another. Pigs are usually slaughtered on arrival, as holding them in pens is stressful for these animals. The animal should not be beaten or manually restrained.

Setting Up the Equipment

After prepping the animal, make sure that all your equipment is easily accessible to ensure you work efficiently. The organization will make the process smoother.

Holding or Stunning Area

The stunning or holding area should be small to prevent the animal from running away. Additionally, the animal should be stunned between the eyes for a swift and painless death. You can draw an imaginary symbol to mark the spot. If the animal has been properly stunned, it should not blink when you touch the eyes or make a sound, and the pig should not be breathing rhythmically.

The Bleeding Process

Immediately after stunning, the pig will kick vigorously. These kicks are unpredictable, and you should always know your knife's position when proceeding to bleed the animal. Follow the procedure below for effective gutting;

- Roll the animal over to have its belly side pointing up towards the sky to access the underside.

- Using your fingers, run your hand over the animal and locate the sternum

- Pointing the tip of your knife towards the tail, insert the knife just behind the sternum.

- Afterwards, twist your wrist 45° and take the knife out. Blood should immediately come out. If not, repeat this motion again until it does. The animal will bleed out quickly as the movement targets a major artery, the carotid artery.

Hanging the Carcass

It is best if you use your tractor, but if that is not an option, then use a pulley system. Use the ropes or chains around the hocks, but be careful as the animal could slip from the entanglement. Alternatively, you could make a neat incision on each side of the pig's leg to make use of the tough tendon on the hock joint. However, be careful as you might cut into the tendon, and the carcass might fall.

Scalding

Once you have safely mounted the carcass on a hook, the next step is scalding. From its hanging position, lower the animal into hot water, preferably 150° F, and continually move the animal to remove hair. If you submerge it into the water without constantly turning it, the meat will start to cook.

After a few minutes, begin scraping and peeling hair from the carcass. If you do not have a large tank to submerge the carcass in, then use a couple of towels dipped in hot water for the same results.

Should you choose to keep the feet, then use a clip to remove the toenails. If scraping becomes challenging, pour hot water on the surface. If necessary, use fire from a torch to remove the hair, but be careful not to burn the carcass.

Skinning

Skinning a pig is, in many ways, like skinning a deer. Be careful not to contaminate the carcass during the process. Use a sharp knife, keeping the sharp side of the blade pointed from the carcass to prevent any sort of damage, including contaminants to the meat. Some people prefer to operate using one clean hand and one dirty hand. Should you use this approach, do not confuse either hand as you could be risking meat contamination. Start skinning the pig from the legs as you make your way to the center of the carcass. If the pig was male, then you will need to remove the penis as well.

Remove the Head

Make your way to where you would consider the backside of the carcass. At the base of the pig's head, make an incision that exposes the backbone (vertebrae). This is where the saw will come in handy as you will use it to separate the head from the rest of the body. A knife will work, but it requires a skillful hand.

Keep cutting until you are met with the trachea, which is a rigid structure punctuated by a couple of cartilage rings. Keep cutting until the head is finally separated from the body.

Gutting

Also known as evisceration, gutting is the next step after skinning and removing the head. First, you should remove the bung, commonly known as the anus. Cut around this area by using the knife. Careful not to cut ham from the leg muscles. The bung should feel loose. Remove it and place it to the side to continue gutting.

Make your way to the belly, where the back legs meet and hold your knife in an adjacent position to the length of the pig. Avoid stabbing the carcass as this only damages the meat and possibly punctures the intestines and other organs. This should open the body to allow space for the insertion of a hand. Insert a knife with the hand inside the belly and make sure the blade is at a right angle to gut the carcass down to the sternum. Once open, continue gutting other areas carefully to avoid damaging any internal organs.

Inspect the Carcass

The organs are essential to your target market. Thus, it is best to first inspect these organs before proceeding. Check for any signs of damage, illness, or infection. Start with the liver and check for any signs of parasitic infection. There will be small white lines to indicate a possible parasitic infection. The heart might have abscesses if it is unhealthy. Generally, look for anything that looks unusual. For instance, the lungs will have hard lumps, which indicate malignant nodules. They grow rapidly in the lungs and indicate cancerous cells. Should you want to keep organs such as the kidneys, heart, or even liver to yourself, you must separate them. Remove the gallbladder first and gently pop the kidneys out. They usually have a thin membrane to peel back when doing so.

Remove Fat (Leaf)

Pigs are known for their high-fat content. None more so than the area near the abdominal cavity. Leaf fat is the large fat deposit found in the pig's inner abdominal lining. For commercial purposes, it is essential to remove this fat. You can do it yourself as this task is fairly simple. Start by separating the fat from the muscle by carefully using your blade. Be careful with your hand placement to avoid injuries. Leaf fat has many purposes; one of them is making lard. If you have no use for this fat, then dispose of it.

Rinse the Carcass

Before rinsing the carcass, cut through the pelvic girdle that opens up between the back legs. If the carcass of the pig is fairly young, then this process should be easy. Mature or older pigs are a little rigid. You may have to use a saw during this process. After that, use a saw to break the sternum in half so the backbone is the only thing holding the carcass together. While facing the inside of the carcass, split it into two by forcing a sharp saw through the backbone. Check the firmness of the hanging carcass to avoid any injuries.

After that, you can comfortably rinse the carcass using hot water. Spray the carcass using a garden sprayer bottle filled with 2% acetic acid. Mostly found in white vinegar, acetic acid helps in fighting the development of a bacterial infection. Check the concentration before starting.

Preserve through Cooling

As mentioned above, you will need a large cold freezer or a cold storage unit to fit the entire carcass. The temperature should be as low as 38° F. If a cold room is not an option, then it would be best to chop the carcass into smaller pieces. It is advisable to have four manageable pieces from each side of the carcass for cooling. Put these pieces in plastic wrap before putting them in coolers for a recommended period of 24 hours. Remember, the carcass pieces need to be properly iced to ensure preservation occurs. Avoid wrapping the carcass pieces. Ensure there are spaces around the carcass pieces to have them properly cooled. Remember to keep your hands clean

Dispose of any Unwanted or Inedible products

There are certain parts of the carcass you should dispose of as most people do not have uses for them. For instance, some organs, the head, the hide, and feet. It is advisable to have a disposal pit for such purposes. But first, contact local authorities to discover the provisions for animal disposals.

In 2015 alone, there were over 100 million hogs slaughtered to provide meat for commercial purposes. As a result, it is important to know the level of meat production with which you are working. Small scale pig keepers should consider slaughtering the animals themselves because it makes sense financially. However, there are some do it yourself questions (DIY) that you might have, as explained below.

Is it Possible to Outsource Pigs to Be Slaughtered?

Butchering animals is not everyone's cup of tea – and rightly so. Purchasing all the equipment is a costly endeavor that you might not be ready to make. Additionally, the skills to butcher a pig take years and years of practice before finally getting everything right. Here, is it beneficial to consult a local butcher for his/her services?

Outsourcing is fine, but you need to consider a couple of factors. For instance, how many pigs do you want slaughtered? If they are many, then you will need to have a large truck or trailer to fit them all. The main challenge in transporting these animals is that they become stressed. Stress can negatively affect the quality of the carcass. Stress leads the body into secreting stress-related hormones, which could have a detrimental effect on meat quality. Also, have the pigs relaxed 12-24 hours before slaughter.

Second, you need to consider the total price of slaughter. One advantage of doing it yourself involves cost-effectiveness. Remember, the aim is to save as much as possible while minimizing the costs.

Chapter 10: Twelve Tips for Your Pig Raising Business

To be a pig farmer for business only requires a small investment in equipment and buildings. It offers quick returns due to the marketable weight of the pigs. Pigs are considered one of the most efficient animals to breed. They produce more live weight from a feed than any other meat producing animal.

Making money from rearing pigs is not about the number of pigs you own but how well you manage the animals you have. It's also not about the number of sows you are breeding; it's the number of piglets she raises and the cost.

Many people ask how many pigs one needs to make it profitable or to support them. This is not an easy question to address due to the number of variables. It all depends on how well you understand your pigs, the nutrition of the pigs, and the market expectations. For example, herding 100 sows that give you malnourished litters with poor carcasses will render your business a failure. Breeding 20 sows that produce two big litters per year can be profitable.

There are several questions you should ask yourself before embarking on this business. Know:

1. Where are you getting the pigs?

2. Where are you getting the feed?

3. Where is the closest custom slaughterhouse?

4. Where is the closest livestock auction?

Profitable big farming is not as easy as we would like it to be. Different challenges can afflict the pig farmer—the growth rate of the litter, the number of piglets a sow can birth, the size of the litter, and even tainted pork. With the tips outlined below, you can take your farming to the next level:

1. Why Start Pig Farming?

The profitability of this business depends on the form of the meat you want to sell. When butchered, the pig yields more than half pure meat. One pound of pork is sold at around $4. The average pig weighs 265 pounds and will, in turn, give 146 pounds, so it can result in a $511 profit.

There are other ways to make money from pig rearing other than selling pork. Pig farmers can opt to sell newborn pigs or sell manure used as fertilizers. It depends on you, the best source of income. Pig meat processed to make sausages is a worthwhile cause. It is vital to note that the profitability of the swine business depends on grain and hog prices.

2. Know Your Market/Identify Your Buyer

The most important question to ask yourself before you start your farming business, is there a demand? Who will buy your pigs once you rear them? Once you have figured out the answer to this question, then you can decide on the breed that will be most suitable. You can either sell weaners, baconers, or porkers. Baconers fetch a higher price, but it costs more to rear the pig to its standard size.

If you have just learned about pig farming, weaners are the best option. The pigs have just been weaned and weigh a little less than 40 kg. They are also faster to produce and more cost-effective. You must calculate properly to pay your expenses before you sell one pig. Also be aware of the profit margin as it fluctuates every year.

The market prices fluctuate depending on the pork supply. This also affects the price of feed, especially maize. The meal will heavily influence your total production cost.

3. Buying Your First Pig

It is more beneficial to pay more for a good pig rather than pay less for a lesser one. You must properly examine the pig before making any purchases. The following are some of the questions you should ask:

- The age of the pig
- Previous ailments
- Vaccination Rounds
- Is it an adult?
- Reason for selling

Check the pig while it's lying down. Observe whether it is comfortable and relaxed. Check the breathing of the animal; the chest should be the one contracting and expanding, not the belly. You can check the reactions of the pig by making sudden noise or whistling— the pig should look at you if it is healthy.

Examine the animal while it's standing up. How is the weight of the pig? Is it too fat or too skinny? If the hips, shoulders, ribs, and backbone are visible, then it's too skinny. If there are fat rolls in its neck, then it's too fat. Too fat is not a good indication as it can fail to breed well; it also indicates that it may suffer leg and foot problems. Be keen to check coughing, diarrhea, constipation, sneezing, and itching.

It is crucial to check to see if the pig's back is straight. The coat should be glossy, the skin should be healthy and clean, there shouldn't be swelling on the head, body, or limbs, the legs of the pig should be straight and strong.

4. Methods of Raising Pigs for Profit

There are many ways to rear pigs. You can use pens, concrete slabs, pastures, or even wooden settings. You need not begin with a large hog growing operation to make a considerable profit. But you will need to know how the pigs will be raised.

Secure homestead fencing for your land. If you prefer electric fencing, you must train your pigs not to touch the wire. You can build the fence from boards, posts, and pallets. The pigs in a natural setting may root and feed as nature intended; then grain can be added to stimulate growth.

The period of buying a feeder pig to selling it can take from six to eight months. There is a vast market for a small farm size. Confined pigs raised commercially are not as tasty as pork from small farms.

5. Pig Breeds for Business

Four profitable pig breeds will secure your business. They are:

a) Large White

This is an excellent choice when starting your pig business. The animal is extremely large, lean, and active, can adapt to different climatic changes and has a long life. The large white is also well known for its quality bacon and pork production. The best characteristic are its ability to crossbreed with other pigs and efficiently produce the best meat.

b) SA Landrace

This is a local indigenous breed that is famous for its high potency. The pig can live on any terrain as its disease intolerance is very high. It's a great choice if you want to supply locally.

c) Duroc

It is popular amongst small scale farmers who want to utilize the carcass of the pigs. The pig has a high ratio of turning fat into carcass fat. It has one of the best qualities of meat, as it is juicy and tender.

d) Kolbroek

It is an indigenous pig much smaller than most modern pigs. It has sturdier legs, strong feet, and very hardy. It is famous for its foraging skills and converting high-roughage rations.

The pigs listed above are the best breeds when you want to start your pig business. They are efficient and thus guarantee a high return if appropriately maintained.

Feeder pigs are seasonal and are not highly required. The best season for pigs is in the spring. Pigs are not as popular in the colder months, so it is not a good idea to raise those pigs in woods or pastures. The show season is more prevalent in the spring season. The time for feeder pigs its essential to consider the price and availability.

6. Pig Products

A suckling pig can be sold between the ages of two to six weeks old. It is the most common ingredient in sausages. Other parts of the pig are used as food products such as the sides for bacon, the shoulders and legs.

a) Internal Organs

The internal organs can be used for pet food, heart valve surgery, and insulin (the pancreas).

b) Pig Skin

The skin of pigs can be used to make collagen for plastic surgery. The collagen is also beneficial in manufacturing energy bars, butter, x-ray film, bread, and drug capsules. Tattoo artists use pig skin to practice their skills.

c) Pig Bones

It can be used for a variety of things, including wine corks, inkjet paper, concrete, fabric softener, train brakes, beer, wine, and even ice-cream.

d) Pig Fat

Pig fat is used for soap, biodiesel, crayons, and shampoo.

e) Pig Blood

It can be utilized for making cigarette filters, fish foods, toothpaste, and colorant in some ham types.

f) Bristles and Ears

Pig bristles are used to make pig brushes, and the pig ears are utilized in chemical weapon testing.

7. Pig Feed

Remember, the nutrition of your pigs highly affects the growth rate and general health of the pigs. To produce good quality pork, invest in the feed of the pigs. Different pigs require different nutrition. These are the different groups:

- Boars and pregnant soars
- Pigs three to ten weeks
- Pigs above 60 kg
- Sows with piglets

Make sure that the protein, vitamins, minerals, and digestible energy are in the right quantities before feeding the pigs. It is advisable to mix the feed on your farm instead of buying readymade. Consult an expert before deciding. Make sure that the pigs always have access to clean and fresh water.

Pigs can eat all sorts of food waste, from commercial kitchen scraps to grazing the land. You must find a reliable source for your pigs. Many people prefer bagged or milled feed from a local store or mill.

The feed from mills is much cheaper compared to buying bags of feed from the store. Make sure that if you are picking feed from the mill, take enough for two to three weeks.

8. At What Age Should You Sell?

Feeders are sold to producers or farms that want to breed them to market weight. They usually weigh between 35 to 50 pounds. They are usually very young and are fresh from weaning. The feeder pigs are not expensive to feed.

Growing hogs, also known as finishing hogs, are over 50 pounds and are being fed for market weight. Growers tend to bring in more money, but they will need more feed as well. Know the age of the piglets and weight before labeling them. Breeders comprise gilts and boars. One boar can serve a few gilts and sows.

9. Costs Involved in a Pig Business

Your profit depends on the number of piglets your sows will produce. To achieve maximum profit, you must be able to ensure that the sows have the highest number of litter, and they are well marketed. You will need:

- Proper housing

Housing will allow you to rear your pigs efficiently and comfortably. Make sure that your house is well maintained and cleaned. Infrastructure must be accounted for in raising a pig.

- Disease control

Ensure that you can control the spread of diseases easily. The conditions on your farm must be clean, and you should take precautionary measures.

- Feed

Pigs are extremely productive animals, they grow well, and their feed is efficient in helping the pigs produce great carcasses. The meal is the biggest concern for most small-scale farmers. To minimize the cost of feed, you will need to be keen on preventing wastage, select a cost-effective feed, and on occasions, mix your own feed.

Additional Costs

- Transport
- Fuel
- Veterinary bills
- Medication
- Slaughter fees
- Freezer
- Repairs and maintenance fees
- Labor
- Additional animals

Other miscellaneous costs vary from worming medications, iron injections, and straw bedding to help you in the care of the pigs.

10. The Need for Marketing

It is crucial to create a marketing plan for your business. Note that market weight pigs can sell through auctions and processing plants. For more profit, consider selling lightweight roaster pigs for holidays, feeder pigs to youth exhibitors, and purebred to producers. You can explore other avenues such as butcheries, grocers, farmer's markets, and restaurants. There are also organic meal delivery services that seek well-bred pork from small scale farmers.

It is essential to consider your digital marketing opportunities. You can build your own branded website, list your business in electronic directories, offer online promotions, and advertise online.

11. Need for Skilled Labor

The farrowing process requires a skilled worker so as the sows can give birth and ensure a healthy litter. It is vital that the pigs are fed daily, vaccinated, treated from parasites, and their pen kept clean and maintained. These services are required throughout the year for the pig's well-being. There is a need for careful selection of the pigs to ensure maximum profit.

12. Selling Options for Your Pigs

There are different options when you want to sell your pigs. You can utilize live auction, direct customers, and retail cuts. People who sell their pigs directly to customers rarely are affected by the stock market. When the stock market plummets, there can be a need to participate in live auctions to support the business.

Selling Through the Livestock Auctions

There are plenty of people who love homegrown pork as opposed to buying from commercial farms. The taste is better from the meat of these farms. There isn't a lot of market for people who want to buy pork from chain stores.

Selling Direct Customers

The best way to keep customers' money in your business is to sell directly to the consumer. For your business to flourish, you will need to invest money into marketing, sales, and schedules. You can opt to sell your pigs whole, half, or in pieces on retail. If you opt to sell your pork in retail, you will need a farm label from a slaughterhouse so it can have a wider reach.

Commodities depend on supply and demand in the market. When the prices are low in the market, the producers stop producing to stimulate demand. As a small-scale farmer, keep the costs in check. If you are selling to the private market, then you will not be affected by the private market. When investing in any market product, know the trends and pricing.

Here's another book by Dion Rosser
that you might like

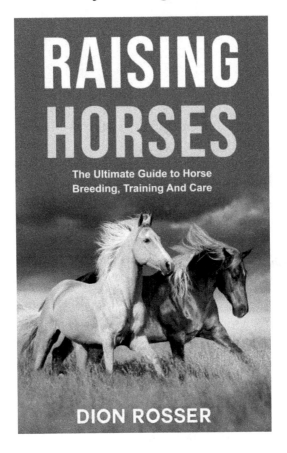

References

Board, N. P. (n.d.). *Safe Animal Handling*. Pork Information Gateway. http://porkgateway.org/resource/safe-animal-handling/

Cooperative, S. S. (n.d.). *5 Great Pig Farming Tips | Southern States Co-op*. Www.Southernstates.Com. https://www.southernstates.com/farm-store/articles/5-great-pig-farming-tips

Feeding The Pigs. (2014, April 2). The Elliott Homestead. https://theelliotthomestead.com/2014/04/what-to-feed-a-pastured-pig/

Handling and Restraining Pigs. (2019, October 8). Thepigsite.Com. https://www.thepigsite.com/articles/handling-and-restraining-pigs

How To Butcher Pigs (At Home On The Farm). (2014, October 14). The Elliott Homestead. https://theelliotthomestead.com/2014/10/how-to-butcher-pigs/

Is Pig Farming Profitable Business? 2020 Market Analysis. (2019, September 19). BusinessNES. https://businessnes.com/is-pig-farming-profitable-business-market-analysis/

Norris, M. K. (2015, March 13). *10 Reasons To Raise Pigs*. Real World Survivor. https://www.realworldsurvivor.com/2015/03/13/10-reasons-to-raise-pigs/

Pig Breeds: A Handy Guide to Choosing the Best. (2019, April 19). Reformation Acres. https://www.reformationacres.com/2018/01/choosing-pig-breed.html

Pig Pens or Pig Pastures. (2014, July 25). Timber Creek Farm. https://timbercreekfarmer.com/pig-pens-or-pig-pastures/

Raising Pigs: Pros & Cons. (2014, December 11). The Prairie Homestead. https://www.theprairiehomestead.com/2014/12/raising-pigs.html

Reproductive Biology 101. (2003, February 15). National Hog Farmer. https://www.nationalhogfarmer.com/mag/farming_reproductive_biology

Snyde, C. W. (n.d.). *How to Butcher a Homestead-Raised Hog - Sustainable Farming.* Mother Earth News. https://www.motherearthnews.com/homesteading-and-livestock/how-to-butcher-a-homestead-raised-hog-zmaz82sozgoe

What are the Benefits of Raising Pigs? | White Mountains Livestock Blog. (2019, January 23). White Mountains Livestock Company. https://www.whitemountainslivestock.com/blog/swine-blog/general-tips/what-are-the-benefits-of-raising-pigs/

Printed in the USA
CPSIA information can be obtained
at www.ICGtesting.com
LVHW082035041123
762998LV00006B/536